HIGH PLAINS
OF NORTHEASTERN NEW MEXICO

*A Guide to Geology
and Culture*

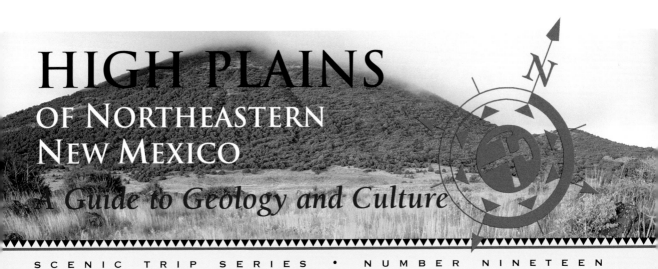

HIGH PLAINS
OF NORTHEASTERN NEW MEXICO
A Guide to Geology and Culture

SCENIC TRIP SERIES • NUMBER NINETEEN

by
William R. Muehlberger
Sally J. Muehlberger
L. Greer Price

New Mexico Bureau of Geology and Mineral Resources

A division of New Mexico Institute of Mining and Technology

Socorro, New Mexico
2005

A Division of New Mexico Institute of Mining and Technology
Daniel H. López, *President*

801 Leroy Place
Socorro, NM 87801- 4796
(505) 835-5420
geoinfo.nmt.edu

ISBN 1-883905-20-6

DESIGN & LAYOUT: Christina Watkins, Amanda Summers
CARTOGRAPHY & GRAPHICS: Leo Gabaldon and Tom Kaus
GIS SUPPORT: Glen Jones
EDITING: Jane C. Love and Gina D'Ambrosio
SERIES EDITOR: L. Greer Price
COVER PHOTOGRAPHS: Front cover: Capulin Mountain ©George H.H. Huey. Back cover: *Arrival of the Caravan at Santa Fe* from the 1844 edition of Josiah Gregg's *Commerce of the Prairies*. New York Public Library.

Scenic Trip 19
First Edition 2005
Printed in Canada

The geology
of the Valley
of the Dry Cimarron
is passing strange.

—LAVERNE HANNERS, *THE LORDS OF THE VALLEY*

PREFACE

Geology, the science of the earth, embraces many specialized fields. Among these are petrology, stratigraphy, geophysics, mineralogy, paleontology, geochemistry, geochronology, and volcanology. Several or all of these specialized fields may be used to interpret the geologic history of any particular locality. In addition to solving fundamental problems dealing with the history of the earth, the geologist, through careful geologic mapping and examination of the rocks, can indicate areas of possible economic importance. These may include the best places to drill for water or oil, the possible extent of metal deposits, the nearest place to find material needed for highway construction or repair, the best location for a dam, or the location of commercial deposits of lime, clay, sand, or gypsum.

HIGH PLAINS
northeastern new mexico

scenic trips to the geologic past

capulin mountain
clayton
raton

Geologic projects in the area of this trip were initially designed to study the availability of ground water in Union and Colfax Counties (the "Dust Bowl" of the 1930s was only a few miles to the east). From such studies the farmer can determine whether there is an adequate supply of water for irrigation (and where he can find it), the rancher knows how far he has to drill to find the small quantity of water needed for his stock, and cities and villages can tell where to locate additional good water to satisfy the demands of their expanding populations. These same studies can also aid in the evaluation of other mineral resources of the area. The information gained from this work is then published so that it may be available to all interested persons. Such publications are often necessarily technical, but many of the features that are described are the same features that attract thousands of people every year to view the scenic wonders of the southwestern United States.

In order to share in the understanding and thus further the enjoyment of these geologic features, the New Mexico Bureau of Geology and Mineral Resources has for fifty years published a series of books titled "Scenic Trips." These regional, field-oriented guides offer an in-depth but popular look at geologic landscapes throughout the state. They also include information on cultural history and historic features as well; few places offer so compelling a glimpse of the connection between geology and culture as the state of New Mexico.

The first edition of this guidebook was published in 1961. Since then, more specialized studies have detailed the origin and variety of the more than a hundred volcanoes and extensive lava flows in this region, as well as their radiometric ages (earlier field studies determined the sequence of eruptions but offered little detailed knowledge of the ages of these eruptions). The sedimentary rocks exposed along the walls of the Dry Cimarron River have been analyzed in great detail and related to other rocks of the same ages across many states. The present volume represents a substantially revised, expanded, and redesigned version of the now out-of-print Scenic Trip # 6.

The first edition of the High Plains *Scenic Trip*, by William Muehlberger, Brewster Baldwin, and Roy Foster, appeared in 1961.

In addition to two chapters on the volcanic and geologic history of the region, the present volume includes four detailed road logs (trips) along routes through the High Plains of northeastern New Mexico. They describe the geology of much of that part of the state as seen from the major state and federal highways. The road logs indicate distances between points of interest and a running total of the mileage covered on each log. Suggested stops are strategically placed where the geologic features that have been seen can be reviewed. The logs can be used independently, but they complement each other to make one grand tour of the entire area.

To fully appreciate the trips, and to have time for your own spontaneous stops, we recommend a full day for each of them. Please respect private property, never disturb archaeological and historical sites, and do not remove any artifacts. For those of you interested in additional information, we've provided a list of *Suggested Reading* at the end of the book.

If you are unfamiliar with the use of road logs, read the section titled *Reading the Log* in Chapter 3 before starting a trip. Many of these trips are in remote areas, so be prepared. Keep your gas tank full, carry water, and drive carefully. Safety should always be your primary concern. Never stop in the middle of a road, and pull off only where there is room (and it is safe) to do so. Drive safely, tread lightly, and enjoy the scenery!

The bureau's publishing program is one of its most effective outreach efforts.

A NOTE ABOUT GEOLOGIC CONVENTIONS

Geologists, like most scientists, follow the rules of their trade, some of which may be unfamiliar or seem cumbersome to the lay person. We have tried to simplify these as much as possible, but perhaps a word of explanation is necessary. Most formal geologic names for rock units (formations) are capitalized: the Raton Formation, for instance, or the Dakota Group. Formal names for volcanic rock units (like the Clayton Basalt) are similarly capitalized. Of course, not all geologists agree on the conventions that should be followed—for instance, what we now call the Chinle Group was for many years in eastern New Mexico referred to as the Dockum. When using formational names less formally (as in Dakota sandstones or Clayton-age basalts) we have not capitalized them, but we felt it made more sense in many places to refer to (say) Dakota sandstone rather than sandstones of the Dakota Group. Although we've tried hard to eliminate jargon from the text, there is a glossary in the back for those terms that are unfamiliar. When all is said and done, it's the ideas that are grand and inspiring, but we have tried to honor geologic conventions wherever possible.

Table of Contents

INTRODUCTION 1

CHAPTER ONE
VOLCANOES OF NORTHEASTERN NEW MEXICO 3

CHAPTER TWO
GEOLOGIC HISTORY OF NORTHEAST-ERN NEW MEXICO 11

CHAPTER THREE
THE SCENIC TRIPS 18

TRIP 1 — Raton to Clayton via the Dry Cimarron River 19

TRIP 2 — Des Moines to Capulin by way of Folsom 53

TRIP 3 — The Dry Cimarron River to Clayton 65

TRIP 4 — Clayton to Raton via US–64/87 71

Suggested Reading 87

Glossary 88

A Word About Maps 91

Index 92

Photo & Figure Credits 97

Acknowledgments 98

About the Authors 98

Geologic Column 100

Geologic Map of Northeastern New Mexico ....inside back cover

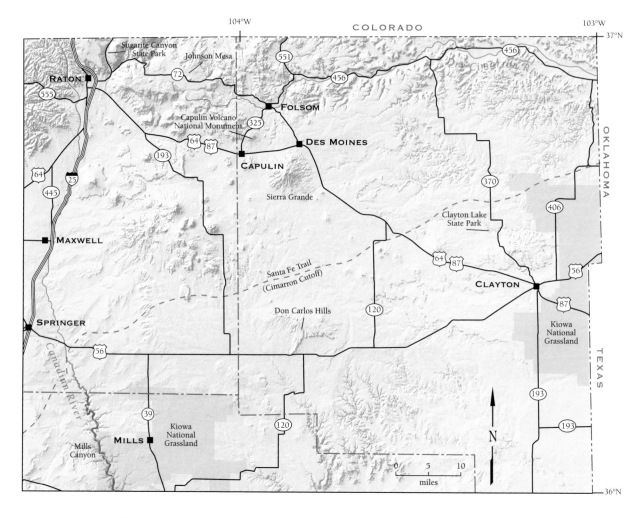

Abandoned homestead on Johnson Mesa.

INTRODUCTION

Much of northeastern New Mexico is covered by vast sheets of lava that flowed from more than a hundred now extinct volcanoes found in this region. The volcanic eruptions started about 9 million years ago and continued intermittently until very recent times. In some areas, such as along the Dry Cimarron River and around Raton, there is an opportunity to observe the much older rocks that underlie the volcanic cover, including spectacular exposures of Mesozoic rocks.

This region has a rich prehistoric and cultural history. Dinosaurs left hundreds of tracks 100 million years ago as they foraged for food in the coastal plain next to the ancestral Gulf of Mexico. Volcanoes erupting across this region produced the largest volcanic field east of the Rocky Mountains during the past 9 million years (and they may erupt again in the near future). About 10,000 years ago early man roamed this region hunting a species of bison that is now extinct. He has been named Folsom Man for the first locality where his arrowheads were found embedded in bison skeletons near the town of Folsom. This discovery in 1927 pushed the history of man in North America back many thousands of years. Bison migrations continued into the nineteenth century, until the advent of railroads gave hunters easy access and drove the herds almost to extinction.

Spanish expeditions crossed this region in search of gold and were followed by Santa Fe Trail merchants in search of trade. The great U.S. exploration teams that crossed the West were searching for resources and routes for travelers to the West Coast. Cattle ranchers brought their herds into and across this region on the famed Goodnight-Loving Trail. Dick Wooten developed a toll road across Raton Pass that functioned until the advent of railroads. Coal mining was a major business that supplied the railroads until the era of diesel engines. Coal continued to be mined for use in smelters until recent years. This region also had its share of "bad guys" who met untimely ends. Both Zane Grey and Max Evans wrote stories set in this region.

As if that weren't enough, northeastern New Mexico encompasses some of the most attractive scenery to be found in the southwestern United States, from gently rolling grass-covered ranch lands to lofty volcanic peaks; from high mesas to deep, colorful canyons. At opposite ends of the area are the small, hospitable cities of Raton and Clayton. It is our hope that this guidebook will add to your understanding and enjoyment of this fascinating region. Naturally, the federal interstate highways are governed by the shortest distance between two points and the path of least resistance, a combination that usually takes you away from the more scenic areas. We hope that this book will tempt you to leave the more frequented paths to see parts of New Mexico only rarely visited.

CHAPTER ONE

VOLCANOES OF NORTHEASTERN NEW MEXICO

Perhaps more than any state in the U.S., New Mexico offers a record of volcanic activity that is enormously diverse. These volcanoes range in age from remnants of older Precambrian volcanoes to eruptions that are (geologically speaking) very young. Volcanic rocks cover about one-fourth of the area covered by this guidebook. The Raton-Clayton volcanic field, which is the focus of this guidebook, is the easternmost volcanic field in North America. It covers nearly 8,000 square miles. Even within this single volcanic field, there are opportunities to see a great diversity of volcanic features.

The rocks are mostly basaltic and consist of lava flows (commonly called "malpais") and piles of cinders and volcanic centers from which many of these eruptions issued forth. Northeastern New Mexico is part of a larger volcanic province that extends northward into the southeastern portion of Colorado, eastward into the Oklahoma panhandle, and westward across New Mexico into Arizona. Just in the area covered by this book, more than a hundred volcanoes have been recognized. All of them have been active intermittently for the past 9 million years (from Miocene to Recent time), and there is no reason to believe that activity has ceased completely.

CLASSIFICATION OF VOLCANOES

Geologists classify volcanoes according to their shape and origin into shield volcanoes,

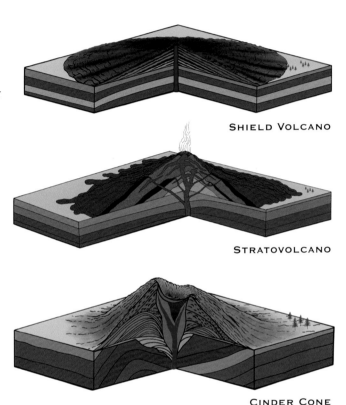

SHIELD VOLCANO

STRATOVOLCANO

CINDER CONE

stratovolcanoes, and cinder cones. These shapes tell us whether the eruptions were relatively quiet or very explosive. We also can tell how fluid the lava was—as thick as molasses in January, or as thin as molasses on a hot day in July.

SHIELD VOLCANOES A very fluid lava that allows its contained gases to escape easily will flow rapidly away from its point of eruption. Successive layers will tend to be

OPPOSITE:
Aerial view of an old grass-covered lava flow, with pressure ridges evident on the surface. Capulin Mountain is in the middle distance, cinder cones dot the horizon.

Mt. Taylor in northwestern New Mexico is an eroded stratovolcano.

Many of the lava flows in the Raton-Clayton volcanic field initially occupied stream valleys or other topographic lows. The hardened flows, more resistant to erosion, now cap the high mesas in the region.

was so fluid, it often failed to form a mound over the vent, and in some areas the vent itself cannot be found. When hardened, the lava is more resistant to erosion than are the underlying sands and shales. The cap of lava thus protects the soft rock under it from wind and rain, so that the stream valleys into which the lava once flowed now stand as the high mesas above the modern stream valleys. Johnson Mesa, Oak Canyon Mesa, Larga Mesa, Clayton Mesa, and others show this inversion of topography (the old stream valleys are now high areas) in northeastern New Mexico.

thin and widespread. The slope of the layers will be low. As this type of lava freezes, it builds a broad, gently sloping cone that is called a shield volcano. The best known examples of this type are Mauna Loa and Kilauea on the Island of Hawaii. An example in Union County, New Mexico, is Mt. Dora (also known as Cieneguilla del Burro Mountain, near the village of Mt. Dora). Sierra Grande, the largest volcano in northeastern New Mexico, is probably of this type. Although the steepness of slope of Sierra Grande suggests that it may be intermediate into the stratovolcano group, that steepness is probably the result of the composition of the lava.

Lava flows from these broad, low shield volcanoes cover large areas. Because the lava

STRATOVOLCANOES Volcanic material that erupts more violently freezes in the air and lands as solid material. The largest pieces are still soft and bend when they hit. Some of the pieces are shaped like bullets and bombs, although most are irregular. This type of material, ranging in size from dust to fragments 5 or more feet long, is collectively called pyroclastic rock to distinguish it from flow rock. Pyroclastics can build steepwalled cones because of the shapes and sizes of material involved (like a giant heap of sand and gravel).

Stratovolcanoes (sometimes known as composite volcanoes) have steeper slopes than shield volcanoes because the eruptions were violent enough that considerable

INVERSION OF TOPOGRAPHY

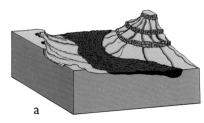

a

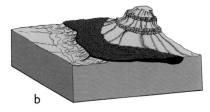

b

c

amounts of pyroclastics, as well as lava, were erupted. A cross section through a stratovolcano shows alternating layers of flow rock and pyroclastic rock. Thus the outer slope gets steeper as you go up the cone. Stratovolcanoes vary in shape and size, depending on the relative proportions of pyroclastic to flow rock and on how much volcanic material was erupted. Many of the most famous volcanoes in the world are stratovolcanoes: Mt. Fujiyama, Japan; Vesuvius, Italy; Mt. Etna, Sicily; Mts. Lassen and Shasta, California; Mt. Rainier, Washington; and many others, including Mt. St. Helens. The best known example in New Mexico is Mt. Taylor. Many of the prominent peaks of the Raton-Clayton region belong in this group. Erosion of the cones since their eruptions has destroyed the typical shape, but the remnants show that they are composed of both pyroclastic and flow rocks. José Butte, Sierra Clayton, Rabbit Ear Mountain, and Laughlin Peak are examples of small stratovolcanoes, although they all tend to be closer to the next variety.

CINDER CONES The best preserved volcanoes in northeastern New Mexico, and the youngest, are those composed only of pyroclastic material: the cinder cones. The fact that these are called cones and not volcanoes indicates that they are generally small. Capulin Mountain is an outstanding example of this type of volcano. The road spiraling up its side is notched into the cinder cone, and the layering of the cinders is visible in the cuts along that road. Twin Mountain, Baby Capulin, and Horseshoe Mountain (all visible from Capulin Mountain) are also excellent examples of cinder cones. Capulin Mountain erupted

about 56,000 years ago. Purvine Hills and Twin Mountain are younger and have been dated at about 50,000 years old. Baby Capulin is the youngest volcano in this sequence of eruptions, but its age has not been determined. Horseshoe Mountain (5 miles south of Capulin Mountain), is about 44,000 years old. The youngest volcanoes dated in this region are Trinchera Creek center, at 13,000 years and The Craters, dated at 12,000 years. Associated with the cinder cones are lava flows that poured out of cracks in the base of the cones rather than spilling over the top as in shield volcanoes and stratovolcanoes. Because cinder cones are too weak to hold together under the pressure of lava filling it to the rim, they break, and lava pours out the base.

Twin Mountain in 1956. Since this picture was taken, much of Twin Mountain has been removed for cinders.

Any of the above volcano types can erupt from a long crack in the ground or fissure rather than a round hole. The volcano would then be elongated along the direction of the crack. An excellent example of this is Twin Mountain, a typical fissure vent with associated cinder cones (in this case the Purvine Hills). Linear strings of volcanoes are indications of vertical, magma-filled fractures along which lava rose to the surface. Many alignments of volcanoes can be demonstrated in northeastern Union County. The outstanding example is the Don Carlos Hills in southwestern Union County. Here 16 extinct volcanoes lie along a line 14 miles long, a perfect example of a fissure eruption. Other good examples of alignments are Baby Capulin, Twin Mountain, and the Purvine Hills; the vents between Mt. Dora and Rabbit Ear Mountain; and the string of volcanoes extending west-northwest through Sierra Clayton. These linear features are all aligned west/northwest throughout this region.

age basalts, the slightly younger Clayton-age sequence of flows poured forth. These are represented by extensive areas of basaltic rocks between Clayton and Sierra Grande. The more silicic rocks of Sierra Grande, Laughlin Peak, and Red Mountain probably also represent Clayton-age eruptions. The most recent phase of volcanic activity is represented by the Capulin-age flows and cinder cones, including Capulin, Baby Capulin, and Mud Hill.

PRESENT FEATURES OF VOLCANIC ROCKS

The older flows, such as the Raton basalts, now have smooth, grassed-over

Many of the volcanoes in northeast New Mexico erupted along fissures, like this modern fissure eruption in Hawaii. Note the cinder cones in this photo.

VOLCANIC SEQUENCE OF NORTHEASTERN NEW MEXICO

The various flows and pyroclastic deposits found in northeastern New Mexico have been grouped into three major periods of eruptions. The earliest of these is the Raton sequence of flows that now caps the high mesas east of Raton (including Johnson, Oak Canyon, and Black Mesas). Following erosion of the Raton-

upper surfaces with only scattered outcrops of basalt. The basalt cliff that rims the high, basalt-capped mesas represents only the lower part of the flow; for the ground rises beyond the cliff. Evidently the more porous and broken basalt in the upper part of the flow has been weathered back from the margin, pressure ridges (which form as the molten lava cools on the surface of the flows) have been weathered down, and low

A DETAILED LOOK AT THE VOLCANIC DEPOSITS

For those who are more familiar with the technical details concerning the origin and nature of these volcanic rocks and wishing to know more, the following detailed description will provide some of the specifics regarding composition.

The most abundant rock type is "transitional," a mildly alkalic, low-potassium olivine basalt, analogous to continental olivine tholeiites. Silica content is near 50 percent. These basalts cover the broad mesas of the Raton and Clayton basalts; they must have been very fluid and voluminous flows. Good exposures of this type of transitional olivine basalt are found on Johnson Mesa or the mesa edges north of Clayton.

Found interlayered with or capping the above are alkali olivine basalts. Instead of only olivine phenocrysts, these contain olivine, orthopyroxene, and rare plagioclase. Rabbit Ear Mountain and many of the eroded cones and shields between the towns of Capulin and Clayton are of this type.

Mafic feldspathoidal volcanic rocks are minor in amount but are represented by the younger Clayton Basalt. They contain phenocrysts of olivine, orthopyroxene, and haüyne, in a groundmass containing nepheline. Most are found in deeply eroded vents in an area near Capulin Mountain; most of these vents are difficult of access. The most convenient one to sample is the Bellisle Mountain flow where it crosses the highway on Johnson Mesa at mile 18.2, trip 1A.

Sierra Grande is unique in being by far the largest volcano in the region (nearly 8 miles in diameter and rising 2,100 feet above the plain) as well as being the only two-pyroxene andesite in this volcanic province. A low roadcut along the east side of Sierra Grande exposes a flow from Sierra Grande (Trip 4A, mile 41.5).

Red Mountain Dacite (silica content 65-70 percent) contains phenocrysts of hornblende and plagioclase. It forms a small number of plugs and domes with short, thick flows. However, none of these are exposed along the public roads of the region.

The final group of basalts, represented by the Capulin Basalt, are silicic alkali basalts and basaltic andesites. They contain abundant olivine phenocrysts, variable amounts of partially resorbed, reversely zoned plagioclase, and large quartz grains (xenocrysts). The best sampling locality is the tip of the flow from Capulin along US 64/87 (Trip 4, mile 51.9).

Haüyne crystal in basalt

Weathered basalt

Vesicular basalt

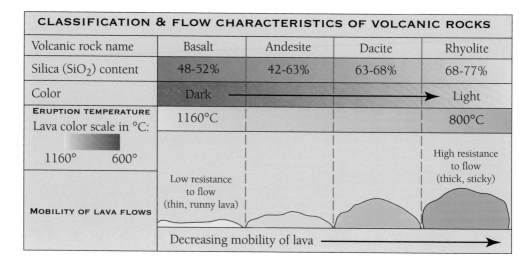

CLASSIFICATION & FLOW CHARACTERISTICS OF VOLCANIC ROCKS

Volcanic rock name	Basalt	Andesite	Dacite	Rhyolite
Silica (SiO$_2$) content	48-52%	42-63%	63-68%	68-77%
Color	Dark ———————————————————→			Light
ERUPTION TEMPERATURE Lava color scale in °C: 1160° 600°	1160°C			800°C
MOBILITY OF LAVA FLOWS	Low resistance to flow (thin, runny lava)			High resistance to flow (thick, sticky)

Decreasing mobility of lava ———————————————→

The color and flow characteristics of volcanic rocks depend very much upon their composition.

places have been largely filled by eroded pieces of volcanic rock and wind-blown sand, silt, and dust-sized material. Ditches for sewer lines in the town of Clayton have shown that the surface of malpais is uneven, although the present land surface is smooth.

Probably all of the flows originally had a rough surface; the true malpais is characterized by pressure ridges and natural levees such as those seen in the more recent flows from Capulin Mountain. The Capulin-age flows that cover the broad flats and valleys

Pressure ridges in lava southwest of Capulin Mountain.

of the present land surface have scarcely been modified by geologic processes in the few thousand years since they were formed. The pressure ridges, which form on the surface of the flows shortly after their extrusion, are easy to discern on these younger flows.

The older volcanic centers have also been considerably modified by erosion. Rabbit Ear Mountain, outside of Clayton, is a good example; the southwest flank is all that remains of the outer surface of the original volcano. Sierra Clayton, south of Grenville and west of Mt. Dora, is better preserved, although the crater has been breached by streams. Robinson Peak and José Butte are similar in preservation to Sierra Clayton. Older volcanoes have been almost completely destroyed by erosion. These have been recognized as volcanic centers only because they stand somewhat above the surrounding land and because loose cinders are found in the vicinity. On the other hand, the most recent volcanoes are scarcely modified by erosion. Capulin Mountain has been set aside as a national monument because it is such a perfect example of a cinder cone.

An interesting feature of many of the cinder cones is that the crater rims are low on the southwest or west sides. This asymmetry suggests that when the volcanoes were active, the prevailing winds were from the southwest or west, and the cinders tended to accumulate on the opposite downwind flank.

A quick glance at a regional geologic map reveals a northeast-trending string of young volcanoes, anchored at the northeast end by the Raton-Clayton volcanic field but extending southwest through the Valles

caldera, Mt. Taylor, and on into Arizona. The feature has been called the Jemez lineament. One question that has puzzled geologists for a long time is why the young volcanoes in this part of the world are distributed in this linear pattern. Several theories have been offered. Although there's no simple answer to this question, clearly the answer must involve some major structural feature deep within the earth's crust. It may well be that a better understanding of the Precambrian rocks, their origin and structure, will provide the answer. In any case, it is with the older Precambrian rocks of northeast New Mexico that we begin our story.

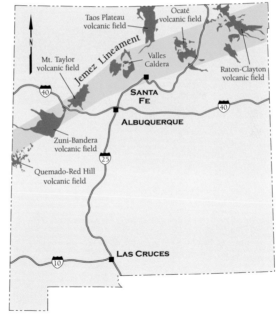

The Jemez Lineament is defined by a string of prominent northeast-trending young volcanoes, which extend north into Colorado and south into Arizona.

CHAPTER TWO

GEOLOGIC HISTORY OF NORTHEASTERN NEW MEXICO

The oldest rocks known in northeastern New Mexico are the Precambrian granites, gneisses, and schists exposed in the Sangre de Cristo Mountains, west of Raton. These rocks are buried east of the Sangre de Cristo Mountains and have been warped down into a deep trough under Raton called the Raton Basin. The eastern limb of this basin is the Sierra Grande arch, a structurally high element where the Precambrian basement granites have been brought to roughly 4,000 feet above sea level along a line that trends nearly parallel to the Colfax-Union County line. East of this line the basement surface slopes downward to below sea level near the Texas-Oklahoma border. These rocks range in age from 1.8 to 1.4 billion years.

The Sierra Grande arch apparently has been uplifted several times since the Precambrian, because we find evidence of materials being derived from it and deposited in nearby areas. This is particularly well demonstrated in Union County, where several wells have penetrated all the sedimentary rocks to the Precambrian and have enabled us to outline the geologic history of these early times.

Early Paleozoic rocks are neither well represented nor well known in this area. Cambrian and Ordovician marine limestone and sandstone are found only in the eastern part of Union County. Mississippian marine limestone extends across the older lime-

stones into central Union County. The Late Pennsylvanian uplift of the Sierra Grande arch, as well as part of the area now occupied by the Sangre de Cristo Mountains (the Ancestral Rocky Mountains), produced a tremendous amount of clastic rocks—arkoses, mudstones, conglomerates, and sandstones—that were spread in broad floodplains across northeastern New Mexico. The Sierra Grande arch supplied some of the earlier materials to the region of Union County and probably supplied the eastern part of Colfax County as well before it was buried by the tremendous mass of alluvial detritus from the ancestral Rocky Mountains to the west. Much of this is part of the

OPPOSITE:
Camptosaurus, the most common of the Morrison-age ornithopods, stood 15–18 feet high and probably weighed close to 2000 lbs.

Major structural features of northeast New Mexico.

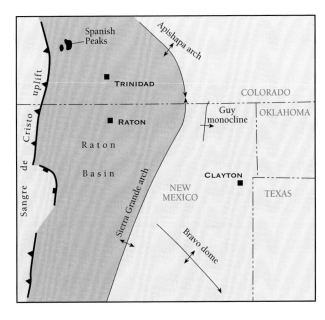

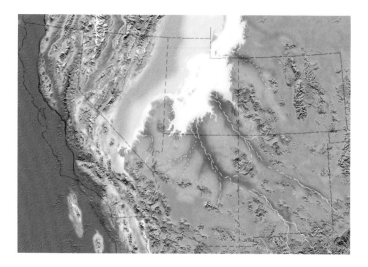

At the beginning of the Mesozoic, 240 million years ago (above), much of New Mexico was dry. By the Late Cretaceous, 75 million years ago (below), the Western Interior seaway, which had inundated portions of New Mexico for over 60 million years, was withdrawing to the northeast.

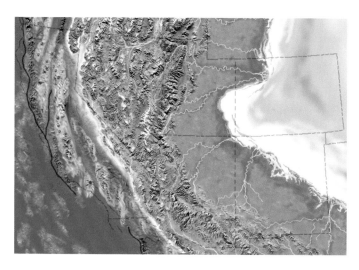

Sangre de Cristo Formation, which underlies all of Colfax and Union Counties and is exposed along the east front of the Sangre de Cristo Mountains.

This formation is overlain by thin layers that were deposited near shore in a shallow arm of the deep Permian sea that occupied southeastern New Mexico and west Texas. Evaporites, such as gypsum, and sandstones and mudstones of the nearshore and continental facies of the Permian sea make up what is now called the Yeso Formation. These rocks are overlain by a marine sequence of limestone, gypsum, and sandstone that constitutes the San Andres Formation. These are the same rocks that we see in the Permian Basin in southeast New Mexico, where they have been producing oil and gas for more than 75 years. These strata are responsible for much of the mineral wealth of the state. All of these rocks in northeast New Mexico were slightly folded, warped, and eroded before the deposition of rocks of Mesozoic age.

This part of the continent entered the Mesozoic Era fairly dry. The Ancestral Rockies to the west continued to shed material across this region of the High Plains. Throughout the Four Corners region, in fact, thick exposures of Mesozoic terrestrial deposits—windblown sands and brightly colored shales—account for some of the most striking scenery in the Southwest. In northeast New Mexico these Mesozoic rocks are generally sandstones and mudstones of floodplain origin, material derived from the ancestral Rockies and spreading out in broad, long river flats. Triassic rocks are the oldest rocks exposed in this region. They rarely contain dinosaur bones in eastern New Mexico, but the tracks of some of these dinosaurs have been found in several places. The most extensive set of tracks is found in sandstones of the Cretaceous Dakota Group exposed in the spillway at Clayton Lake, 10 miles north of Clayton (Trip 3, mile 37.0).

At the close of Triassic time, the sediments were slightly warped and eroded before they were covered by sediments of Jurassic age. The Jurassic rocks begin with the Entrada Sandstone, a sand dune deposit, probably near a shallow sea or lake. Brown silts of the overlying Summerville Formation represent lake-bottom deposits. Most of the overlying Morrison Formation consists of the typical floodplain silts and muds of slow, sluggish streams. During Cretaceous time the sea once again gradually encroached upon this area. The Purgatoire Group at the base of the Cretaceous interval consists of a lower sandstone (probably nearshore marine deposits) overlain by a dark gray clay or mud layer (offshore marine deposits). This is overlain, with a slight unconformity, by river deposits derived from the Rocky Mountain region, a middle portion that contains some coal, and an upper portion of marine sandstone. The upper sandstone was deposited in a sea that covered most of west-central North America during the final invasion of marine waters into the interior of the continent. The thick black shales (Niobrara and Pierre) and thin dark limestones (Greenhorn and Fort Hays) seen in the Raton area, were also deposited in this sea.

The end of the Mesozoic marks one of the most striking discontinuities in the fossil record. The Cretaceous/Tertiary boundary was marked by massive extinctions worldwide. Perhaps 50 percent of the species alive at the time did not survive into the

Cenozoic. This included the dinosaurs, whose presence had dominated the planet for millions of years. Although there is still some debate about the exact nature of this mass extinction, most geologists feel that ultimately it coincided with a cataclysmic event: the collision of our planet with an asteroid or comet, in the vicinity of Mexico's Yucatan peninsula. The presence of extraterrestrial material associated with this collision has been identified in Cretaceous/Tertiary deposits around the world. The so-called "K/T boundary" is exposed in a few places in New Mexico, in the Raton Formation,

The end of the Mesozoic, in New Mexico and around the world, was marked by a catastrophic event: the collision of a large asteroid or comet with our planet.

most notably in rocks along I-25 through Raton Pass, in at least one isolated spot in Sugarite Canyon State Park, and (most easily seen) in an outcrop of this formation atop Goat Hill, just outside Raton (see page 23 for details).

There are few rocks of Cenozoic age in this area, but events of that part of geologic time can be inferred from studies of areas to

THE HIGH PLAINS AQUIFER

The Tertiary Ogallala Formation here at the western edge of the Great Plains is part of what is known as the High Plains aquifer. The High Plains aquifer, shown here in blue, is the most wide-

spread blanket sand-and-gravel aquifer in the nation. It underlies 174,000 square miles, including portions of eight states: New Mexico, Texas, Oklahoma, Kansas, Colorado, Nebraska, Wyoming, and South Dakota. This aquifer supplies drinking water for 82 percent of the people who live in the High Plains, but its major use is for agriculture: 94 percent of ground water withdrawals from the aquifer are used for irrigation. This makes the High Plains aquifer the most intensely pumped aquifer in the nation, yielding approximately 30 percent of the nation's ground water used for irrigation.

The supply of water in the High Plains aquifer is not unlimited, however, and in most places the recharge rate—from precipitation, surface streams, and return flow from irrigation—is far lower than the rate at which the water is being withdrawn. In recent years there has been in most places a substantial decline in the water level within the aquifer. In New Mexico the aquifer is already largely depleted. Much effort is currently being directed toward a more detailed understanding of the High Plains aquifer, including some prediction of its lifespan at current rates of depletion. Given that this region is responsible for 19 percent of the total US production of wheat and cotton, 15 percent of our corn production, and nearly 18 percent of US beef production, the future of the High Plains aquifer has become an issue of national concern.

the west, in and near the Sangre de Cristo Mountains. The Late Cretaceous sea, in which were deposited the Niobrara Formation and the Pierre Shale, began to drain off near the end of the Cretaceous period. Uplift in or west of the Sangre de Cristo Mountains evidently began late in the Cretaceous Period and continued to the end of the Eocene Epoch. The non-marine sediments of latest Cretaceous and early Tertiary age, now exposed in the big cliffs near Raton, were derived from rocks in the uplifted area and were spread as shoreline and continental deposits eastward toward

and perhaps into Union County. Although the uplifting may have originally consisted largely of upwarping, in the late Eocene it involved intense folding and thrusting. By the end of the Eocene Epoch the gross features of the eastern part of the Sangre de Cristo Mountains were formed. Piedmont deposition east of the mountains continued until about the end of the Eocene Epoch after which the region was eroded by streams. Mild deformation and the formation of the Sierra Grande arch as it is today occurred at the time of the folding and thrusting in the mountains to the west. In the Chico Hills area of southeastern Colfax County thick sills of igneous rocks were intruded at this time.

EVOLUTION OF TODAY'S LANDSCAPE

East of the Sangre de Cristo Mountains, erosion during the Oligocene and Miocene Epochs produced a rolling plain, sloping eastward and possibly southeastward from the Raton region. In the vicinity of Clayton local relief on this plain was as much as 200 feet. Except in local areas where limestone beds served as protective caps to preserve soft shale hills, streams east of Sierra Grande arch removed most of the soft Cretaceous marine shales and limestones down to the resistant sandstones of the Dakota Group. In parts of the south panhandle of Union County, and in monoclinal warps, erosion exposed beds as old as the Jurassic Morrison Formation and the Triassic Chinle Group. From late Miocene into the Pliocene Epoch, and indeed almost to the present, there was continued uplift of mountain blocks, forming the present-day mountains of north-central New Mexico. As a result of this mountain building, the Rio Grande structural trough formed and was filled with (Santa Fe Group) sediments eroded from the rising mountains. The streams draining the eastern flank of the Sangre de Cristo Mountains deposited an extensive blanket of upland deposits—clay, silt, sand and gravel—east of the mountains. This material, mostly the Ogallala Formation, was deposited at first in valleys and, as the valleys filled, covered the low hills of the mid-Cenozoic piedmont plain. As a result, the late Cenozoic sediments rest on different Mesozoic formations in different places.

Recent isotopic age determinations on the volcanic rocks of this region give us the opportunity of detailing the more recent geologic history. Volcanic activity began about 9 million years ago, when Raton-age basalts flooded down broad stream valleys that today are high mesas: Fisher's Peak, Horse Mesa, Johnson Mesa, Oak Canyon (Kelleher) Mesa, forming the platform for the younger Emery Peak volcano. These eruptions ended about 8 million years ago. The lava flows from that early episode of volcanism have effectively buried and preserved the upstream end of drainage systems that have long since been eroded away elsewhere. Later erosion has largely removed

The lava that hardened to form this erosion-resistant basalt cap occupied topographic lows when it was extruded onto the landscape, a classic example of inversion of topography.

Today these lava-capped ridges are a common landform in this part of New Mexico.

over 2,000 feet of rock (including the Ogallala Formation) near Raton. Projecting the preserved valley shape under the basalt flows to the west shows that the valleys intersect the mountain front at altitudes of about 9,500 feet—well above the highest points in the intervening region.

The youngest of these early basalt outpourings 7.3 million years ago produced the linear Larga Mesa and Kiowa Mesa, tiny in comparison with the earlier eruptions. This was followed 6.5 million years ago by small-

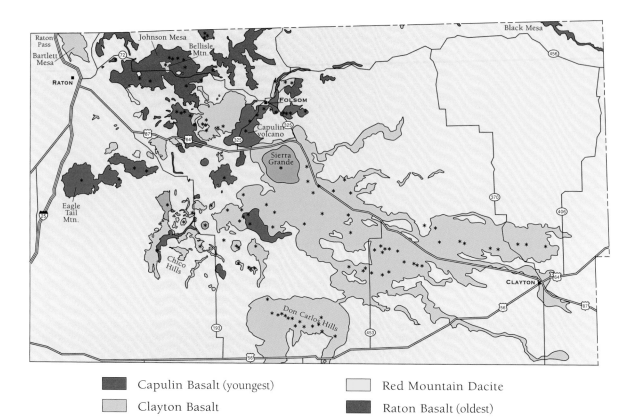

■ Capulin Basalt (youngest)

□ Clayton Basalt

□ Sierra Grande (Clayton-age)

□ Red Mountain Dacite

■ Raton Basalt (oldest)

* Vents

The oldest volcanic deposit of the Raton-Clayton volcanic field is the Raton Basalt, which first erupted about 9 million years ago. The youngest deposits are the Capulin-age vents, which are as young as 12 thousand years.

volume rhyolitic eruptions in a band from Red Mountain and Towndrow Mountain on Johnson Mesa south to Laughlin Peak and Palo Blanco Mountain. These rhyolitic eruptions were followed by more massive floods of basalt that produced Mesa de Maya, mostly in southeastern Colorado, and the Yates flows at the southernmost part of this volcanic field. Both flows erupted about 5.0 million years ago and are included in the Raton basalts. Colorado's Mesa de Maya flow extends into the northeast corner of New Mexico and the northwest corner of Oklahoma, where it remains the highest point in that state.

This was followed by the eruption of two very different and distinct types of

magma. At 4.03 million years ago, Bellisle Mountain (Dale Mountain on some recent maps) erupted lava (with distinctive bluish crystals of haüynite) that flowed off Johnson Mesa and down the Dry Cimarron River to a few miles past Folsom. Other vents of this composition are found near Capulin Mountain and, although not dated, are presumed to be about the same age. The last of the Raton-age basalts (compositionally the same as the earlier Raton Basalt) erupted 3.6 million years ago and cap Bartlett Mesa above the city of Raton.

Then the largest eruptions of the region began. The Clayton-age basalts constitute the second of three major periods of eruption. The first eruption of this Clayton-age sequence was of Sierra Grande, which covers 43 square miles and rises 2,100 feet above the surrounding plain. It has a unique composition for this region: a two-pyroxene andesite. No flows extending beyond the base of the mountain have been identified. Dates from four different locations on the mountain (including the summit crater) average 2.67 million years. The huge Clayton Basalt flows then poured forth; today they extend eastward for 40 miles and almost completely surround Sierra Grande. They cover 295 square miles and occupy many ancient drainages that reflect the trends of the earlier Ogallala drainages. The Clayton basalts range in age from 2.3 to 2.4 million years. Rabbit Ear Mountain is one of the vents for this episode of eruption. Rows of eruptive centers along the flow suggest that an east-southeast trending series of vents erupted to produce this large flow.

Gaylord (Carr) Mountain and Yankee Volcano basalts erupted 1.7 and 1.1 million years ago. These basalts contain haüyne, a feldspathoidal mineral that appears as small blue crystals in hand specimens of the basalt. The presence of these crystals indicates a silica-poor magma. Because of their age, these are now included in the third major period of eruption: the Capulin phase of volcanism (this in spite of differences in their composition). Capulin basalts range in age from 1.44 million years old (the unnamed flows at mile 4.8 on trip 4B) to only 13 thousand years old at Trinchera Creek center, on the New Mexico-Colorado state line—practically yesterday, geologically speaking. Capulin Mountain, the most prominent cinder cone from this phase, erupted 56,000 years ago (although a radiocarbon date on charcoal found beneath the

Capulin Mountain flow suggests that Capulin may be as young as 22,000 years).

Downcutting and formation of local alluvial deposits accompanied the volcanic activity. This downcutting has left the oldest lava flows as the highest above modern stream levels, with progressively younger flows at lower elevations. These ages give us the opportunity to more fully understand the evolution of drainage patterns and stream captures through time.

The 4.0 million-year-old Bellisle basalt flow came off Johnson Mesa and continued east down the Dry Cimarron River valley. Thus, we now know that the Dry Cimarron River valley was already in existence 4 million years ago. It has not grown headward or changed significantly since that time.

The northward growth of the east-trending Canadian River (south of the Scenic Trip area) into the Raton-Cimarron region is less well documented. Bartlett Mesa (above Raton) at 3.9 million years of age is only a few hundred feet below the adjacent 9-million-year-old Fisher's Peak Mesa basalt, and it tilts east-southeast, the same direction as the older mesa, suggesting that the older drainage pattern is still intact. The dated volcanic rocks in the present north-trending segment of the Canadian River are the 1.14-million-year-old Yankee Volcano (just east of Raton) and the 1.0-million-year-old Eagle Tail Mountain (20 miles south of Raton). In both cases, the basalts lie on old river surfaces only a few hundred feet above the modern river levels. Clearly, the Canadian River had captured this region (the broad area west of the volcanic field) long before 1.0 million years ago. How much earlier is yet to be discovered.

CHAPTER THREE

THE SCENIC TRIPS

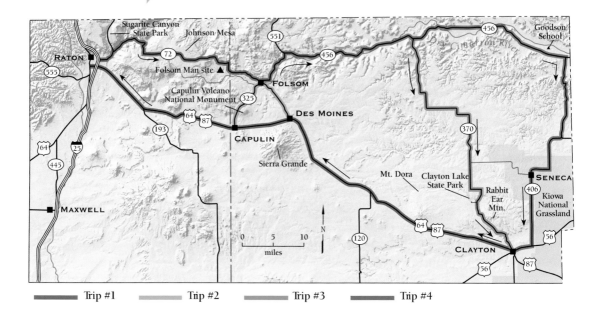

Trip #1 ——— Trip #2 ——— Trip #3 ——— Trip #4

The automobile trip logs in this book include excursions between the cities of Raton and Clayton, with several opportunities for side trips in this vicinity. The logs are designed to be used with your automobile's trip meter: cumulative mileage is shown in black bold type at the beginning of each entry; the mileage between points is shown at the end of each entry. Because odometer readings vary from vehicle to vehicle, check-point mileages such as mile markers, cattle guards, and intersections are included and should also be used as a guide. Many of the trips in this chapter have been broken into smaller legs, in order to allow more flexibility for the user.

Critical directions, warnings, and instructions are printed in bold colored type. Features of interest are pointed out using the clock system. For example, the front of the car is 12:00 (we generally say "straight ahead"), due left is at 9:00, and due right is at 3:00. If an object is identified at 1:00, it is just to the right of straight ahead.

Many of these trips are on public land. Please remember that, in most cases, collecting of any sort is prohibited on public lands. Be particularly careful around archaeological sites: they are protected by law, and (more importantly) they are fragile, and scarce. In places where the road crosses private land, respect landowners' rights, and obey all posted signs.

For obvious reasons of driving safety,

these trips are designed for at least two people: it is the passengers rather than the driver who must follow the odometer and read the logs. Try to read far enough ahead of your location so that the description can be completed before you reach the point of interest. Be sure that you have water and a full tank of gas before starting out. Gas stations are scarce along some of the routes.

When stopping to look at rocks, beware of rattlesnakes and scorpions. Always turn a rock over before picking it up. Never stop in the middle of a road, and pull

straight ahead

your left

your right

behind you

off the road only where time, space, or designated pullouts allow. Be careful of traffic, cyclists, and pedestrians when pulling off the road. Enjoy the trips, and—above all—drive carefully!

READING THE LOG

4.9 MP 3. Road turns right to cross Chicorica Creek. Lake Maloya straight ahead. (0.5)

19.4 STOP 2 - Sheep Mountain Carbon Dioxide Pipeline pumping station on left side of road. From here a spectacular panorama of volcanoes can be seen

Cumulative Mileage, milepost markers noted where they exist

Mileage between points

Critical directions, warnings, instructions

SCENIC TRIP ONE - (132 MILES)
Raton to Clayton in Three Legs

This trip follows the "back road" from Raton to Clayton, along the valley of the Dry Cimarron River, and offers a spectacular variety of scenery and geology. Virtually none of it is visible from the more direct route from Raton to Clayton via US 64/87. For convenience, the trip is split into three legs, as follows:

Trip 1A: Raton to Folsom, 37 miles
Trip 1B: Folsom to junction of NM-456 & NM-406, 58 miles
Trip 1C: Junction of NM-456 & NM-406 to Clayton, 38 miles

A short distance east of Raton, NM-72 abruptly ascends past many abandoned coal mines to the top of Johnson Mesa, a broad, treeless, lake-dotted, gently rolling, grassy plain. At the eastern end of the mesa, the road winds down into the headwaters and upper valley of the Dry Cimarron River, near the site of the original Folsom Man discovery. At the town of Folsom, the route intersects the route through Folsom (Trip 2) that continues on to Capulin Volcano National Monument and US 64/87.

Trip 1B continues down the Dry Cimarron River past a narrows that

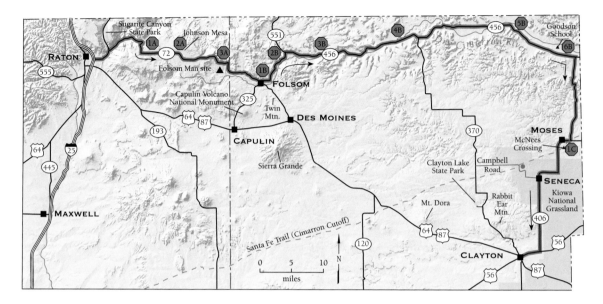

funneled lava flows from the many volcanoes in the vicinity; the sequence of eruption can be determined with ease. This
route also passes over the oldest rocks
exposed in this region, including the colorful Triassic and Jurassic rocks of Battleship
Mountain and Wedding Cake Butte (on Trip
1C). Just a mile before the road reaches the
Oklahoma state line, the route turns south,
climbs out of the canyon onto the High
Plains and on to Clayton. Ruts of the Santa
Fe Trail and a monument to it are visible
where it crosses this leg of the log.

From Raton, at an altitude of 6,600
feet, the road reaches an altitude of over
8,000 feet on Johnson Mesa, then drops
to about 5,000 feet in the Dry Cimarron
River valley near the Oklahoma state line.
Although a few miles of the road is
unpaved along the lower part of the Dry
Cimarron River segment of the route, it is
well maintained, and, except for short
periods during the winter months and
following heavy summer thunderstorms,

it is readily passable in a passenger car.

The first 10 miles of this route crosses
outcrops of the Cretaceous Pierre Shale and
Trinidad Sandstone en route to Johnson
Mesa. This high mesa is capped by part of a
sequence of Tertiary flows called the Raton
Basalt. These rocks are traversed for about
15 miles to the east end of Johnson Mesa.
As the route descends from the mesa top
into the headwaters of the Dry Cimarron
River, there are limited exposures of sands
and gravels of the Tertiary Ogallala
Formation and of the Cretaceous Niobrara
Shale, Fort Hays Limestone, Carlisle Shale,
and Greenhorn Limestone. Also seen along
this segment are extensive exposures of a
sequence of Tertiary basalt flows younger
than the Raton basalts that have been
grouped together as Clayton Basalt. In the
valley below Johnson Mesa is a third large
group of eruptive rocks that are called
Capulin Basalt. This last group represents
the youngest series of eruptions in northeastern New Mexico. A discussion of the

complex sequence of flows in this area is included in Trip 1B.

Continuing down the valley of the Dry Cimarron River for another 59 miles (the Oklahoma border), the oldest Cretaceous rocks present in the area, consisting of the Dakota and Purgatoire sandstones, cap the mesas on both sides of the valley. Beneath these resistant sandstone cliffs the colorful shales and sands of the Jurassic Morrison Formation form a steep slope ending at the white sandstone cliff of Entrada Sandstone, also of Jurassic age. Low on the canyon walls and flooring the valley of the river are the vivid red shales of the Triassic Travesser Formation. The oldest rocks exposed in northeastern New Mexico, the Triassic Baldy Hill Formation, are seen in the valley floor.

Where the route turns south near the Oklahoma border, the road climbs out of the canyon of the Dry Cimarron River across the Triassic Travesser Formation and the Sloan Canyon and Sheep Pen Sandstones, the Jurassic Entrada Sandstone and Morrison Formation, and the Cretaceous Purgatoire and Dakota sand-stones. Thus in a few brief minutes we have passed over rock units that represent about 100 million years of geologic time. The road then travels across rolling plains cut by some small valleys, including those of the North Canadian and Cieneguilla Rivers, and the ruts of the Santa Fe Trail. The divides between streams are capped by sands and gravels of the Ogallala Formation, the unit that holds up the High Plains of eastern Colorado, New Mexico, and the Texas Panhandle.

SCENIC TRIP ONE-A (37 MILES)
Raton to Folsom

Raton, at an altitude of 6,600 feet, was settled in 1879 with the arrival of the Atlantic and Pacific Railroad (later renamed the Santa Fe Railroad). The extensive coal deposits in the mesas surrounding Raton contributed greatly to the growth of the town during the age of steam locomotives. Today Raton is the central marketing area for a large part of north-central New Mexico, serving many widely scattered ranches and small farms. Industries, in addition to coal mining, include lumbering, manufacturing, and the very important tourist trade.

On the road behind the lighted "RATON" sign west of town (on Goat Hill) is a sign labeled "Iridium layer" that marks the thin layer of debris from the giant meteorite impact in Yucatan that led to the demise of the dinosaurs and perhaps half of all other life forms at the end of the Cretaceous Period, about 65 million years ago.

Raton was first named Willow Springs for two large willow trees that were watered by springs. A government cattle-feeding station was established here in the 1860s. The Atchison, Topeka and Santa Fe (AT&SF) Railroad pushed south in the fall of 1880 and located a repair shop and rest stop at its southern base of Raton Pass. Willow Springs had the best water supply in the region; it was the logical watering place between "Uncle Dick" Wooten's Ranch on Raton Pass and the Canadian River to the south. It was therefore chosen as the division headquarters of the railroad, and the name Raton (named for the pass) replaced the name of Willow Springs. Raton grew as a railroad community; by 1881 the population had reached nearly 3,000.

Called "the Pittsburgh of the West," it became the railroad, coal mining, and ranching center of northeastern New Mexico.

Like other western frontier towns, Raton had its share of violence with lynchings and shoot-outs. But it also had culture and refinement. Raton was a stop on the theatrical circuit in the 1880s, and boasted theaters and an opera house. The town grew near the railroad tracks with stores, restaurants, hotels, and saloons to furnish the needs of the railroad workers. This area is now the Downtown Historic District. First Street is the home of the Scouting Museum of New Mexico, the Historic Santa Fe Depot, and the Raton Museum, which has collections and pictures on Indians, mining, ranching, ghost towns, the history of the Wooten Toll Road, and the railroad.

Raton from the top of Goat Hill.

Raton Pass has been used by travelers since prehistoric times, and it connects southeastern Colorado and northeastern New Mexico. The Santa Fe Trail Mountain Route took the northern circuit out of Bent's Fort, followed Indian trails, crossed Raton Pass near the Wooten Ranch, and ended at Fort Union, New Mexico. The heavy wagons took up to five days to make the trip over the pass. In 1880 the AT&SF railroad laid tracks over the pass at 7,622 feet, the highest point in the line. Today trains travel through a tunnel in the mountains below the pass.

0.0 **Begin in downtown Raton at the junction of Second Street (Business I-25) and NM-72 on the north side of the historic district of Raton. Go east on NM-72, setting your trip meter to zero just as you enter the underpass below the former Atchison, Topeka, and Santa Fe Railroad tracks (now the Burlington Northern Railway). Just ahead you'll veer right following signs for NM-72. (0.6)**

0.6 The road curves left. To the left on the skyline is Bartlett Mesa, capped with basalt. Forming bold cliffs about halfway down are nearly horizontal layers of the light-colored Trinidad Sandstone. The Trinidad Sandstone represents the last stand of the shifting shorelines in the upper Mesozoic rocks of this region. It is also used locally as a marker for coal beds, which represent the terrestrial environment that predominated in this area after the final withdrawal of the sea. There are other sandy formations above the Trinidad Sandstone in this region, but they do not form such bold and continuous cliffs. Straight ahead on the skyline is Johnson Mesa, capped by the older sequence of basalt lava that is included in the group called Raton Basalt. Bartlett Mesa is capped by the younger sequence of the Raton basalts. (0.4)

1.0 MP 1, on the far side of the bridge across I-25. Mileages for this leg of the

The view from mile 1.6.

journey should approximate the mileposts along this stretch of the road. Just beyond, you'll cross a branch of Raton Creek. (0.6)

1.6 At the crest of the hill a roadcut exposes marine black shales of the upper Cretaceous Pierre Shale, capped by stream gravel. An abandoned older valley level rims the valley floor and extends south from the highway. Ahead across the narrow valley, the road climbs onto another terrace, a gravel-capped stream valley remnant. These older valley surfaces are covered with gravel and thus are commonly mined for road con-

THE CRETACEOUS/ TERTIARY BOUNDARY

The youngest exposures of Mesozoic rock in northeast New Mexico are the Raton Formation, which extends across the Cretaceous/Tertiary boundary into the Paleocene. This "K/T boundary" marks one of the major world-wide extinctions in the fossil record. It was in deposits of this age, at this boundary, that scientists from Berkeley in 1980 first identified a layer enriched with iridium. The element occurs naturally on this planet, but the presence of a layer so enriched in iridium was taken as an indication of a collision with an asteroid or comet 65 million years ago. The idea met with considerable resistance but today is widely accepted as fact. In the few places where the K/T boundary is exposed, geologists now note with much

interest the thin clay layer that marks this important boundary in the geologic record.

The Raton Formation is exposed in outcrop on Goat Hill, in Raton. In this outcrop (above) the iridium-enriched layer is visible. To reach these exposures, take Second street north of downtown (past the turnoff to NM-72 east); turn left on Moulton avenue. Follow it for several blocks until you reach a T-intersection. Turn left and follow this road up onto South Mountain Drive. Just a little ways past the turnoff to Goat Hill itself (keep right at that intersection), you will come to a pullout with a picnic table on the right side of the road. You can pull off and park here and examine the adjacent outcrop; a small sign indicates the iridium layer.

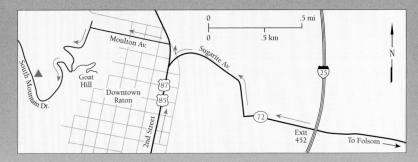

struction material. Johnson Mesa is on the skyline straight ahead; Hunter Mesa, at 12:30; Meloche Mesa (with north tilt) at 10:00. The whole southern skyline is punctuated by extinct volcanoes. (0.4)

2.0 MP 2.0. To the north on the left are light-colored cliffs of Trinidad Sandstone (Cretaceous), rising eastward away from the center of the Raton Basin. (0.3)

2.3 At 11:00 through the gap on the distant skyline is Barilla Mesa, capped by the older sequence of Raton Basalt. Ahead, just beyond where the road turns left and extending to right, are more remnants of the

Lake Maloya, Sugarite Canyon State Park.

SUGARITE CANYON STATE PARK

The entrance to the state park is 2 miles north of NM-72 on NM-526. The Visitor Center, just outside the park entrance, is in the building that once housed the post office for the Sugarite coal camp. The camp was built in 1908 to supply home-heating type coal to as far away as Kansas and Oklahoma and was in operation between 1910 and 1941. The center has exhibits depicting life in the camp when it was at its height with a population of nearly 1,000 people. The camp was composed of many nationalities—Italians, Slavs, Japanese, Mexican Americans and English. It includ-ed a two-story schoolhouse, a company store, doctor's office, and a big multi-purpose club-house. There was a baseball field where teams from other camps would compete with the locals. Each fall a train arrived with box cars filled with grapes that were quickly converted to wine. Mules pulled coal cars in the mine. When the oil industry prospered in the thirties and forties, bringing the use of butane for heating, the camp production came to an end. There are only ruins of the buildings today, with a trail through the camp to mine #2 with signs along the way describing building uses, activities, and camp life.

Sugarite is an anglicized version of the Comanche word meaning "an abundance of birds." The Visitor Center has comprehensive lists available of the wide variety of park birds, butterflies, flowers, and mammals. There are grasslands, oak groves, huge ponderosa pines, picnic tables, trails, boat ramps for fishing (the lakes are stocked with rainbow trout), and tent camping. Because the lakes are the water supply of Raton, only electric-powered boats are used, and no swimming is allowed. In winter tourists can try their luck at ice fishing, or join in the Ice Fishing Derby the first Saturday in February.

Sugarite coal camp near Raton, New Mexico, ca. 1910.

gravel-capped valley we were last on. (0.7)

3.0 Road turns left. Ranch road enters from right. After you've made the turn, you'll see cliffs of Trinidad Sandstone straight ahead. (0.3)

3.3 On the left are embankments of the abandoned Santa Fe Railroad bed to Yankee, a ghost coal-mining community. Roadcuts ahead expose the Pierre Shale capped with stream gravels. (0.5)

3.8 Straight ahead in middle ground is a mesa capped with basalt from Yankee volcano of older Capulin Basalt events (1.14 million years old). Road now follows Chicorica Creek. (0.5)

4.3 On your left are cliffs of Cretaceous Trinidad Sandstone. At the left end of those cliffs is a black dump from a small coal mine. Ahead is Horse Mesa, capped by the younger sequence of Raton Basalt (about 3.6 million years old).

The Trinidad Sandstone is composed of beach and beachfront sands. The overlying Raton Formation consists of sands and muds of river, floodplain, and swamp deposits. The swamp deposits, originally mostly plant debris, were compressed into

coal. The numerous coal mines of this canyon are found in those six-foot-thick coal beds, which are usually less than 100 feet above the Trinidad Sandstone—the prominent cliff-forming marker bed of the region. The bluffs marking the west edge of Raton are held up by the Trinidad Sandstone. This bluff continues southwest to the town of Cimarron as it marks the southern boundary of the Raton Basin.

The Cretaceous-Tertiary boundary lies within the lower coal beds. This boundary contains evidence of the massive meteorite that struck Yucatan at that time, and which is believed to be the cause of the world-wide extinctions that occurred at that time. (0.4)

4.7 Junction with NM-526 to Sugarite Canyon State Park. Keep right to stay on NM-72. (0.2)

4.9 Road turns right to cross Chicorica Creek. Lake Maloya straight ahead. (0.5)

5.4 Bridge over Chicorica Creek. Pierre Shale is exposed in stream bank on right.

Shales in outcrop tend to be unspectacular, but they're easy to spot. Shale is composed mostly of fine-grained silt and clay, and outcrops of shale weather into mud-covered slopes rather than clean faces where the bedding is clearly visible. Geologists measuring sections through shale often use a trenching tool to locate a clean face. To the roadside geologist, outcrops of shale appear as dull-looking, mud-covered slopes, often sparsely vegetated, with hints of more resistant silt beds poking out through the weathered slope. (0.7)

6.1 Enter Yankee. On the near skyline

Trinidad Sandstone, Sugarite Canyon State Park.

THE ENSIGN RANCH HOUSE

This once-imposing mansion, visible along the road to Sugarite, was built in 1889 by A. D. Ensign, an English promoter and owner of mines and a railroad in nearby Yankee. The estate covered 2,100 acres with fields of alfalfa, orchards, streams, and livestock. The large two-story main house at one time was known as The White House by locals because it was painted white inside and out with a green roof. There were twenty rooms filled with elaborate furniture, five bathrooms, fireplaces in almost every room, white marble statues in each window. The primary means of lighting were coal oil lamps and candles; one can imagine how much soot was added when in later years a coal furnace was installed. Mr. Ensign planned to build two additional guest houses for guests from the east, but they were never built because of a scandal involving Mr. Ensign, and he was spirited away. It was rumored he had swindled money from elderly women in England to finance his project.

straight ahead is basalt from the Capulin-age Yankee Volcano.

Yankee was a coal mining camp founded by the Chicorica Coal Company in 1904. The camp was so named because several financiers from Boston ("Yankees") promoted the Santa Fe, Raton & Eastern Railroad from Raton to Yankee. By 1907 the camp had a population of around 2,000, but the mines began to close and by 1914 the population began a rapid decline. Today only ruins of the camp remain. (0.1)

Trinidad Sandstone is exposed in the cliff behind the Profazi Ranch headquarters.

6.2 Yankee Lodge. (0.7)

6.9 At 2:00 is Yankee volcano. When it erupted about 1.14 million years ago, this valley floor was level with the base of the lava flow that now forms the ridge that extends to 3:00 from the cone. Erosion since the time of its eruption has lowered the valley floor to its present position.

On your left, halfway up the hillside, are several coal mine dumps and head frames. The younger sequence of Raton Basalt caps Horse Mesa above the mines. (0.7)

7.6 County Road A25 enters from right. (0.3)

7.9 Road enters from left. Coal mine dumps on the left. Lowest white bed in Trinidad Sandstone forms prominent cliff from 10:00 to 12:00. Barilla Mesa (9-million-year-old Raton Basalt cap) is on the skyline ahead. (0.4)

8.3 Ranch road to right. The town of Yankee

existed in this area. The town has vanished, but many of the coal mines, some operated by individuals, are still visible on the slopes of Horse Mesa. The region is now devoted to ranching. The few pine trees are all that remain after the early logging operations.

From this point, the gradual eastward climb of the Trinidad Sandstone out of the center of the Raton Basin can be seen by tracing the massive cliffs from on your left up onto Johnson Mesa straight ahead. (1.0)

9.3 The road now begins to climb Manco Burro Pass and ultimately tops out on Johnson Mesa. Scrub oak, ponderosa pine, and cottonwood trees flank Johnson Mesa in this area. (1.0)

10.3 Outcrop of Trinidad Sandstone on the left. (0.8)

11.1 Junction with Road A30 to left over Manco Burro Pass. We keep to right to climb onto Johnson Mesa. (0.5)

11.6 Raton Basalt of earlier sequence (dated at 8.15 million years old) is exposed in roadcuts on the left. This outcrop shows the porous nature of many lava flows caused by gases within the molten rock escaping as bubbles. The rounded shape of the boulders is caused by rain and ice, which decomposes the rock along the fracture surfaces, working inward by sheets, like an onion skin. (0.4)

12.0 STOP 1 - MP 12.0. Stop at pullout on left. We can now see westward to the distant peaks of the Sangre de Cristo Mountains. We can also see the grassy top of Horse Mesa, capped with younger Raton Basalt. To the right is Barilla Mesa, which extends to where we are and is capped with older Raton Basalt. Johnson Mesa, onto which we are now climbing, is also capped by the older Raton Basalt sequence. Clearly seen from here is the rise toward us of the cliffs of Trinidad Sandstone, the base of the coal-bearing sequence in this area. Directly behind you in the distance are the plains of southern Colorado, with Raton-capped Mesa de Maya (dated at 5.1 million years old) on the distant skyline. Mesa de Maya continues southeastward, crosses the corner of New Mexico, and enters the Oklahoma Panhandle, where it is called Black Mesa. (The highest point in Oklahoma, at 4,973 feet, is on Black Mesa.) Towndrow Mountain is at 3:00. (1.2)

13.2 Road A29 straight ahead climbs what appears to be volcano remnants associated

Spheroidal weathering of basalt.

Towndrow Mountain erupted onto the Raton Basalt cap of Johnson Mesa during the eruption of the Red Mountain dacites, approximately 6.8 million years ago.

with the eruptions of the Raton Basalt cap on which we are riding. We keep left on paved road. Road curves left just ahead. (0.4)

Remnants of volcanic vents on Johnson Mesa.

13.6 Cone-shaped Towndrow Mountain (8,609 feet) at 1:00 and Red Mountain at 11:30 are both volcanoes punched through the Raton Basalt cap; both are part of the group named Red Mountain Dacite. At 10:00 and 11:00 are broad hills of Clayton Basalt, which also erupted through the Raton Basalt cap. Lava from Bellisle Mountain (8,520 feet; shown as Dale Mountain on some recent maps) at 11:00 flowed south across Johnson Mesa, then eastward to near Emery Peak, east of Folsom. The eruption of Towndrow Mountain is thought to have occurred about 6.8 million years ago. (0.6)

The panormic view from Stop 2.

14.2 At 12:30 on the skyline is cone-shaped Red Mountain. At 11:00 is Bellisle Mountain, with a microwave relay tower clearly visible on top. During the summer wild iris cover the valley on the left. (3.3)

17.5 St. John's Methodist Episcopal Church on the right. Built in 1897, it is still used for ceremonies during the summer. Diagonally across the road is the cemetery. (0.7)

18.2 Road now climbs onto 4-million-year-old basalt from Bellisle Mountain, visible on the left (note microwave towers on top). (1.2)

19.4 STOP 2 - **Sheep Mountain Carbon Dioxide Pipeline pumping station on left side of road.** From here a spectacular panorama of volcanoes can be seen between 12:00 and 3:00. Starting from Red Mountain, in foreground at 12:30, is Sierra Clayton, over 40 miles away on distant sky-line above right base of Red Mountain; Robinson Mountain at 1:00; Capulin Mountain (8,215 feet) just to right and behind it; Sierra Grande (8,720 feet), the huge mountain on the skyline; José Butte, in front of right flank of Sierra Grande. At 2:00 on the skyline are Malpais Mountain (left) and Horseshoe Mountain (right); at 2:30, triple-peaked Palo Blanco Mountain; then Timber Buttes and Laughlin Peak (8,820 feet) at 3:00. (4.2)

23.6 Excellent view at 10:00 (on the left) over the north edge of Johnson Mesa into

Red Mountain   Robinson Mountain   Capulin   Sierra Grande   José Butte   Malpais Mountain   Horseshoe Mountain   Palo Blanco Mountain

ST. JOHN'S METHODIST EPISCOPAL CHURCH

Johnson Mesa is a lava-capped tableland standing 2,000 feet above the surrounding land and extending 14 miles, most of the distance between Folsom and Raton. It was named for Elijah Johnson, a pioneer cattleman who owned a ranch just south of the mesa. It was seldom used until 1887, when settler Marion Bell brought a group of dissatisfied miners to settle on the high mesa. They were attracted to the area by cowboy reports of rich soil, spring water, abundant sunshine, and beautiful scenery, but they weren't told of the extremely harsh conditions in winter: -30° to -40° F with snows, blizzards, and poor roads. Stone and earth houses were built to protect the families from the weather. Farms of 100-175 acres peaked in 1910. The permanent population decreased rapidly after that. Today, only a handful of hardy families make this their seasonal home.

The only evidence of the town of Bell (the post office was 2 miles to the north) is St. John's Methodist Episcopal Church, and the cemetery across the road. The church still holds services alternately Methodist and Episcopalian. Its dedication on August 14 is celebrated every year.

The stories of two Johnson Mesa families tell the sad tale of hardship. John and Emma Floyd Towndrow (1850-1897) and their family were not prepared for the blizzards and extreme cold the first year. The next year they were better prepared with wood, coal, and a tighter house. They stayed because it was a better life than working in the mines. They grew potatoes as a staple, had one milk cow, and a big garden. Fruit was a luxury, and the greatest Christmas present was an orange. There are five Towndrow gravestones in the church graveyard. (Towndrow Peak, in the area, was named for the Towndrow family).

The graveyard tells another story of hardship. There are several grave markers of the Floyd family, but one group in particular makes a vivid impression. R. and Margaret E. Floyd (1911-1988) buried six of their seven children here before any of them reached the age of four.

Colorado. Columnar jointing of the basalt can be seen along the cliffs. Many lakes and meadows, like the one at the right, are low areas on the tops of the lava flows, broadened and deepened through disintegration and decomposition of the basalt by rain, snow, and vegetation. (0.7)

24.3 View on the left to the plains of Colorado. Cliffs of Johnson Mesa show the successive lava flows that built up the older sequence Raton Basalt cap of the mesa. (1.2)

View looking north into Colorado over the edge of Johnson Mesa, from 24.3. Columnar jointing is visible in the distant cliffs.

Raton Basalt is exposed in the roadcuts on the left as the highway begins the descent off the eastern edge of Johnson Mesa.

25.5 Road starts down off Johnson Mesa, an island in the sky. Roadcuts on the left show the Raton Basalt cap (dated at 7.6 million years old). Platy layering was formed when the lava was still moving yet getting nearly stiff enough to tear. Drive carefully: many curves ahead. (0.6)

26.1 Old borrow pit on left is in orange-colored sands of Ogallala Formation, which underlies the Raton Basalt cap of Johnson Mesa. The Ogallala sands and gravels were deposited by rivers in a broad blanket stretching east from the early Rocky Mountains. This broad blanket of sediments also caps the High Plains from the Texas Panhandle to Nebraska.

Ahead, in the distance, is Sierra Grande, largest volcano of this region; to the right and nearer, with a road spiraling up to its top, is Capulin Mountain. Robinson Peak, just to the right and in front of Capulin, was the last Clayton-age volcano to erupt in this vicinity. Immediately preceding it was José Butte, at 1:00. Preceding these was Bellisle Mountain. Basalt from Bellisle Mountain (behind us on Johnson Mesa) underlies the grassy bench below the skyline that extends from 3:00 around to 12:00. The higher bench on the skyline at 2:00 is capped by Raton Basalt. (1.0)

27.1 STOP 3 - Pullout for historical marker: Folsom Archeological Site. The Folsom Site was discovered in 1908 by George McJunkin, an ex-slave and Texas cowboy who first spotted the bones of a bison sticking out of the wall of an arroyo near this spot. It was not until the 1920s that the site caught the interest of archeologists. Radiocarbon dates on the material eventually confirmed that both the bison skeletons and the points were at least 10,000 years old. This clearly established man's antiquity in the New World, thousands of years earlier than was believed at the time. It continues to be one of the most important Paleo-Indian sites in North America. The site, on the National Register of Historic Places, is some distance from this marker and is not open to the public.

On left is the rim of Johnson Mesa. Ahead on skyline is Oak Canyon Mesa. The Raton Basalt cap of this mesa was formerly continuous with the Johnson Mesa basalt cap. The low cone-shaped hills in the valley below are not extinct volcanoes but are capped with remnants from Bellisle Mountain Basalt (on right) or Raton Basalt (tree-covered hills beyond ranch buildings on left). The valley, known as Hereford Park, is the headwaters of the Dry Cimarron River (so named in order to avoid confusion with the Cimarron River southwest of Raton). (0.9)

28.0 CAUTION, curve right, steep hill. (0.7)

28.7 Road entering from left over Trinchera Pass. This road is impassable in wet weather. Our road turns right down a terrace, a gravel-capped remnant of the early valley floor to the Clayton-age basalt sheets that form the grassy mesa on the other side of the valley. (1.3)

30.0 Low mounds to right of highway are small cinder cones. Lava from these vents filled the valley beyond. Cinders from the flank of one cone are exposed in the road-cut. (0.2)

30.2 Another small vent on left. (0.2)

30.4 On left, easternmost of the four aligned vents known as the Folsom Vents. Basalt from these volcanoes can be seen in the valley at 3:00. The road ahead for the next 0.2 miles is on basalt from this early Capulin Basalt eruption. (0.3)

30.7 Cross stream. White layers visible on right in the creek banks are limestone beds

THE FOLSOM SITE

In 1908 a black cowboy named George McJunkin noticed bones protruding from the side of an arroyo not far from this spot. Likely the bones had been exposed by rapid downcutting associated with the Dry Cimarron flood of 1908 (the same flood that was responsible for the great loss of life and property in the nearby village of Folsom). The bones of what were extinct bison attracted little attention until the 1920s, when scientists from the Colorado Museum of Natural History (now the Denver Museum of Nature and Science) visited the site. Excavations in 1926-27 confirmed not only the presence of ancient bison, but of a number of fluted projectile points (at left) that were clearly of the same age. Even without the radiocarbon dates that would later confirm the enormous antiquity of the find, it was clear that these remains were late Pleistocene in age—far older than any that had been found to date. Radiocarbon dates on the bone would eventually document this age as 10,500 years before present.

The site is what is known as a "kill" site rather than a habitation site; nomadic Paleo-Indian hunters on the Great Plains killed and butchered perhaps as many as thirty-two *Bison antiquus* in this vicinity, spending a few days before moving on. The climate was cooler then, but these drainages associated with the Dry Cimarron River would have been good hunting grounds. An even older (and equally significant) Paleo-Indian site on the Great Plains was found near Clovis, New Mexico. The Clovis site is open to the public.

Although the Folsom site was discovered in 1908, it wasn't until excavations in the 1920s (above and below) that the full significance of the site was known.

in the Fort Hays Limestone Member of the Niobrara Formation. The black shales belong to the overlying Pierre Shale. (0.1)

30.8 Enter Union County; leave Colfax County. (0.7)

31.5 White limestone beds in roadcut on left are part of the Fort Hays Limestone. The valley rim on the right is columnar-jointed basalt from Bellisle Mountain. Roadcuts ahead are in landslide debris of the Fort Hays Limestone. Abundant fragments and whole casts of oysters, clams, and a few cephalopods found in this limestone demonstrate that these rocks were deposited in the ocean. (1.1)

The Fort Hays Limestone beds at 31.5 contain fossils of Cretaceous oysters and clams.

32.6 Hill to the left about 50 feet above the road is capped by the Fort Hays Limestone. The broad valley opening to the left is called Fisher Park. Oak Canyon Mesa, with its older Raton Basalt cap (dated at 8.98 million years old) rims Fisher Park. (0.5)

33.1 Fort Hays Limestone caps the hill behind the windmill. (0.6)

33.7 Road turns sharp right ahead onto terrace cap. (0.3)

34.0 Road turns sharp left off terrace cap. Ahead at the end of the terrace is a high knob of gravel graded to the top of the Bellisle Mountain Basalt that forms the rim on the far side of the valley.

To the right down a small canyon can be seen cliffs of Bellisle Mountain Basalt, which now rims the valley on both sides of the Dry Cimarron River. Dominating the far horizon for much of this stretch is Sierra Grande. It is the largest isolated mountain in North America and the largest volcano in this region. Sierra Grande is nearly eight miles in diameter and rises nearly 2,100 feet above the surrounding plains. It is a two-pyroxene andesite, a composition that is different from all the other volcanoes in this region. It is about 2.5 million years old. The barren volcano in front of Sierra Grande is Baby Capulin Mountain. The forested area in front of it is on basalt from Capulin Mountain (at 1:00). The lower cone to the left of Capulin is Mud Hill. (0.5)

34.5 Thin-bedded brown Dakota sandstone forms rim of valley on left. Ridge on right is held up by Bellisle Mountain Basalt with a thin cap of gravel. Dakota sandstone is exposed in the cut on the right. (0.2)

34.7 Ahead on the skyline is Twin Mountain. So much of this cinder cone has been removed for railroad ballast by the Colorado and Southern Railway that the reason for its name is no longer readily apparent. To the left of Twin Mountain on the skyline are small fissure vents called the Purvine Hills.

On the left at 9:00 is a small outcrop of the orange-colored Ogallala Formation just under the Raton Basalt cap of Oak Canyon Mesa. (0.3)

Twin Mountain today. Compare this with the photo on page 5.

35.0 A tongue of basalt from Capulin Mountain covers the valley on the far side of the Dry Cimarron valley (at 3:00). (1.0)

36.0 Capulin Mountain looms on the skyline behind the ranch buildings that are nestled under the Bellisle Mountain basalt rim. (0.2)

36.2 Road crosses horseshoe bend of Colorado and Southern Railway. (0.3)

36.5 Roadcut in sands and silts of uppermost Morrison Formation. The white coating is caliche, a calcareous coating that forms as a result of weathering. (0.2)

36.7 Junction with NM-456. Turn right to the town of Folsom, or to join Trip 2 to Capulin Mountain. End of Trip 1A.

SCENIC TRIP ONE-B (58 MILES)
Folsom to Junction NM–456 & 406

0.0 Junction of NM-325 and NM-456 at the Folsom Museum. Turn right onto NM-456. (1.0)

1.0 MP 1. The markers begin back in Folsom at the junction of NM-325 and NM-456. (0.7)

1.7 Ruts at left, going into erosion control tank, are the result of military wagon trains carrying supplies to Fort Union from Fort Dodge in the 1870s. This road goes down the valley ahead and turns north up Toll Gate Canyon past Branson, Colorado. To the south the trail skirts the east side of Capulin Mountain, goes through Capulin, and continues southwest to Fort Union (now Fort Union National Monument). (0.1)

1.8 STOP 1 - Doherty Road enters from the right. Pull off the road and park at this intersection. This is a good place to review some of the geologic features visible from here. Volcanic centers and flows that can be seen are Emery Peak straight ahead;

Morrison sandstones in roadcuts at 36.5.

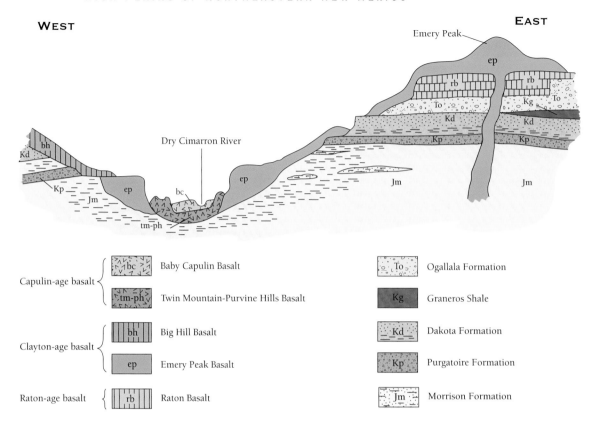

WEST

EAST

Emery Peak

Dry Cimarron River

Capulin-age basalt {
- bc — Baby Capulin Basalt
- tm-ph — Twin Mountain-Purvine Hills Basalt

Clayton-age basalt {
- bh — Big Hill Basalt
- ep — Emery Peak Basalt

Raton-age basalt {
- rb — Raton Basalt

- To — Ogallala Formation
- Kg — Graneros Shale
- Kd — Dakota Formation
- Kp — Purgatoire Formation
- Jm — Morrison Formation

Cross section across the Dry Cimarron River below Folsom, at gorge caused by the dam of Emery Peak Basalt.

Raton Basalt cap with columnar jointing below Emery Peak; Emery Peak Basalt in cliffs below skyline at 11:00; Big Hill in middle distance at 10:00; low mounds from Augite Vents at 4:00; Purvine Hills Basalt on skyline ridge between 2:00 and 3:00; Mud Hill, the tree-covered hill this side of Capulin Mountain; José Butte at 6:30; Capulin Mountain behind you; the Purvine Hills, the low ridges on the skyline at 3:30; Baby Capulin is the nearest volcano this side of Capulin Mountain; Sierra Grande on the skyline at 5:00; and flat-topped Oak Canyon Mesa capped by Raton Basalt to the left (north) at 3:00.

The Folsom sequence of Clayton-age basalt eruptions began with Emery Peak erupting through the Raton Basalt cap and pouring lava northward into Dry Cimarron

River valley. At about the same time Big Hill, East Big Hill, and East Emery Peak erupted. All four of these vents lie on an east-trending line, as if they are part of the same eruption that took advantage of this fissure. These eruptions dammed the river, and into the lake thus formed poured lava from the following volcanoes, in the order named: Augite Vents, Purvine Hills Basalt, Mud Hill, Bellisle Mountain, on Johnson Mesa, 20 miles west (not visible here); José Butte (not visible, behind Robinson Peak), and finally Robinson Peak.

A long period of erosion ensued that was interrupted by the Capulin-age sequence of basalt eruptions. These started with the Folsom Vents (not visible), Capulin Mountain, then Twin Mountain, Purvine Hills, and finally Baby Capulin. This ended

the sequence of eruptions in this area (for now, at least).

Earlier than any of those described is Sierra Grande, and the oldest of all are the Raton Basalts capping Johnson Mesa and Oak Canyon Mesa, and forming the rim below Emery Peak.

Straight ahead, behind the ranch house, are two levels of light-colored sandstone; the lower, which is nearly white, is the Purgatoire Formation; the upper, which is reddish brown and caps the mesa, is the Dakota Group sandstone. These sandstones and the Ogallala Formation sands are the main aquifers of this region. The Dakota scarp is about on the crest of the Sierra Grande arch. The Cretaceous and older rocks are involved in this giant fold; beyond the scarp in front of us these rocks slope gently eastward, with only minor wrinkles all the way to Texas. Coming this way (westward), the rocks slope gently westward into the Raton Basin west of Raton. To drill to the Dakota Group in Raton would require a well nearly 3,000 feet deep. (0.8)

2.6 Roadcut in topmost fill of lake caused by the basalt that flowed from Emery Peak. Ruts on left were formed by military wagon trains of Santa Fe Trail days and later by the Goodnight-Loving Trail herds that moved north along this route. (0.2)

2.8 In gully bottom is Purvine Hills or Augite Vents Basalt (these two and Twin Mountain are identical in all characteristics; they probably erupted simultaneously). (0.4)

3.2 Road turns left through gap cut in Emery Peak Basalt; it holds up the mesa above us on the left. This flow formed the dam for the Folsom sequence of Clayton-age basalts. Note bent ash layers in cuts on right; they were probably deformed by an incoming load of lava and sediments. (0.2)

Emery Peak.

Folsom Falls on the Dry Cimarron River cascades over Baby Capulin Basalt. The plunge pool is in Twin Mountain or Purvine Hills Basalt. Emery Peak Basalt on horizon.

3.4 STOP 2 - Pull off the road into the parking area for the Folsom Falls Fishing Area on the right. Beyond the green gate you can follow a short trail to the waterfall over the Baby Capulin Basalt, with a plunge pool below cut into Twin Mountain or Purvine Hills Basalt. Administered by New Mexico Department of Game and Fish, it is now known as the Folsom Falls Fishing

EMERY GAP / TOLL GATE CANYON

In 1851 Captain John Pope was sent from Fort Union to locate a more direct route to military posts in Kansas. Emery Gap became the route of the military road to Fort Union during the days of the Santa Fe Trail and later the Goodnight-Loving Trail from west Texas/southeast New Mexico to Colorado and Nebraska. By 1865 Emery's family formed a town called Madison, the first permanent settlement in the area. In the years between 1873 and 1875 there was a great volume of wagon traffic, both military and civilian freight moving through, and the town prospered. In the 1870s Bill Metcalf constructed a road with a toll station, through what is now called Toll Gate Canyon. The arrival of the railroad in 1887 caused the wagon route to be obsolete. The Madison residents moved to Folsom to be near the railroad, and Madison became a ghost town.

Area. It is open to the public for fishing (no swimming, camping, or open fires).

Platy columns of Emery Peak Basalt form walls on both sides of the valley; basalt from Twin Mountain, Purvine Hills, and Baby Capulin lies in valley floor. Note the tall columns of Raton Basalt high on the hillside below Emery Peak and the brown, blocky, and massive Dakota sandstone. The cliffs on the left side of the road (to the north) are massive basalt, probably from Big Hill, although basalt from it is identical with the three others aligned with it: East Big Hill, Emery Peak, and East Emery Peak. (0.6)

4.0 MP 4. Basalt to right is Twin Mountain-Purvine Hills type (remember, they are identical in all characteristics, so we can't tell them apart). (0.3)

4.3 On left East Big Hill basalt forms the rim. Ahead brown Dakota sandstone forms the rim with white Purgatoire Sandstone ledge below it. (0.8)

5.1 Emery Peak Basalt flowed down from skyline at 3:00 and filled the Dry Cimarron River valley, whose floor was then above us at the level of the base of the flows forming the mesa ahead of us and the valley rim on the right. Basalt outcrops in stream at right are Twin Mountain-Purvine Hills type. (0.4)

5.5 Ridge on right along road marks the end of Twin Mountain-Purvine Hills Basalt. Beyond this point lava from only Baby Capulin flowed down the Dry Cimarron River. (0.2)

5.7 Ahead at 2:30 the white band of the Purgatoire Sandstone can be recognized. Capping it is the brown Dakota sandstone. On distant skyline at 12:30 is Devoys Peak (6,740 feet), easternmost remnant of the earlier Raton Basalt sequence that extends east from Raton. Baby Capulin Basalt in stream walls on right. (0.4)

6.1 Oak Canyon Road on left. (0.4)

6.5 Emery Peak Basalt holding up spur at right. This is a good place to visualize how the basalt flowed down the side of the valley. The shape of the cliffed valley can be seen under the flow, and the smooth upper surface of the lava flow gives a rounded appearance to the new valley. On the left at

10:30 is white Purgatoire Sandstone overlain by brown Dakota sandstone. (0.4)

6.9 Ranch road enters on right. At 3:30, about 100 yards from the road, is a stone-walled dugout built by the original settlers in the 1870s. Broad mesa at 1:30 is capped by basalt from East Emery Peak. In valley bottom can be seen the ridge of Baby Capulin Basalt. (0.8)

7.7 Junction with NM-551 to Branson, Colorado (to left), up Toll Gate Canyon to Emery Gap. This is the only low pass into Colorado between here and Raton. Madison Emery discovered the route into Colorado while exploring the Cimarron. Keep right.

The Dry Cimarron River canyon is rimmed throughout its length in New Mexico by the Dakota sandstone (brown), which is underlain by the Purgatoire Sandstone (white cliffs). The slopes below these sand formations are generally mantled by landslide debris but in places the greenish, reddish, or purplish silts and muds of the Morrison Formation can be seen. We will also be able to see the white Entrada Sandstone along the foot of the slope under the Morrison. Farther downstream we will see the older red beds of the Chinle Group. The Entrada Sandstone is the eastern extension of the widespread sand dune field that existed in the Four Corners region, hundreds of miles to the west. It is at its thickest in Zion National Park. (1.9)

9.6 On the right, at the left end of the Emery Peak Basalt mesa, is the Triassic Chinle Group (red beds at base of ridge, overlain by Entrada Sandstone (2 white cliffs). Capping these is the lower part of the

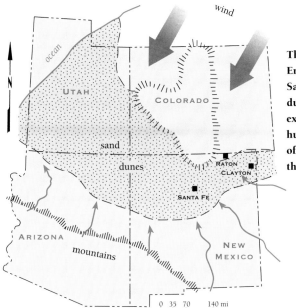

The Jurassic Entrada Sandstone dune field extended hundreds of miles to the west.

Morrison Formation (greenish and reddish siltstones). (0.1)

9.7 In the roadcut can be found small pieces (like bubbles) of red chalcedony in what has been called the "agate bed." This layer, in some places thicker, can be found in the lower part of the Morrison Formation throughout northeastern New Mexico, eastern Colorado, western Kansas, and southern Nebraska. Its origin is not certain, although recent studies suggest that it is glass (dust

Raton Basalt caps mesa on skyline at 9.6. Dakota sandstone forms cliffs in slope below Raton Basalt; Emery Peak Basalt caps low mesa in middle. Triassic rocks are exposed to the left and beyond Emery Peak Basalt.

Cross-bedded Dakota sandstone at mile 11.8.

size) from a stupendous volcanic eruption that was later altered to its present form. If true, this marks the surface of the earth at that instant of time in the states where it is preserved. The roadcut is in the toe of a large landslide. (0.5)

10.2 On the left the familiar double cliff of Dakota sandstone (brown) over Purgatoire Sandstone (white) is well developed. (0.4)

10.6 On the left are large landslide blocks of Dakota sandstone. These have been etched by wind and rain, the better cemented layers standing out as ridges.

The mesa across the valley at 1:00 is capped by the easternmost earlier Raton Basalt (south of Devoys Peak). Under it are very thick cliffs of Dakota and Purgatoire sandstones. (0.9)

11.5 Briggs Canyon entering from right. Basalt from Purvine Hills flowed down at least as far as the narrow mouth of the canyon. Whether it is under this broad alluvial valley is unknown. However, only Baby Capulin Basalt crops out downstream from this point. Low hill in center of the valley is part of the Morrison Formation. (0.3)

11.8 Note the large block of crossbedded Dakota sandstone in the fence line on the left side of the road. These crossbeds are of the type known as torrential and are deposited by rapidly moving currents, usually a river. If the block is right-side up, then the current moved from left to right. (0.4)

12.2 The low red hill at 11:00 beside the road is composed of Triassic Chinle shales. On the left skyline is the spectacular rim of brown Dakota sandstone over white Purgatoire Sandstone. (0.2)

12.4 Ranch road enters from left. On skyline at head of canyon behind ranch house is Devoys Peak. (0.4)

12.8 Irrigation ditch. Stone fence at 9:00 on hill. Baby Capulin Basalt along road on left just ahead. (0.2)

13.0 STOP 3 - MP 13. Ranch road on left; pull off and park at this intersection. The old stone ranch house of Madison Devoy, first settler in this region (about 1870), is still in use on Brown Ranch behind hill. Beyond the house are thin beds of sandstone of the Chinle red beds. (0.1)

13.1 Bridge over Dry Cimarron River. At the edge of the valley just ahead at 1:00 are red cliffs composed of the Chinle Group. (0.9)

14.0 Baby Capulin Basalt dots whole valley floor. Note how thin the Entrada Sandstone (yellow-white sand cliffs low on the valley wall) is in this region. This area was a broad low hill when the sand dunes that now compose the Entrada Sandstone blanketed this area. (0.6)

THE CHINLE GROUP

The Triassic shales of the Chinle Group are perhaps best known from Petrified Forest National Park in eastern Arizona. Here the thick exposures of brightly colored shales contain abundant deposits of petrified wood. The Chinle was deposited in a broad band that extended as far east as northeast New Mexico and the Oklahoma panhandle, where for many years it was known as the Dockum Group or Formation. It is exposures of the

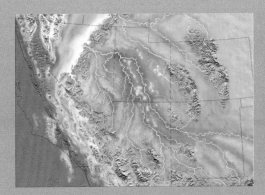

Chinle shales that define the Painted Desert in eastern Arizona (at left) and give it its characteristic look.

14.6 Long ridge of Baby Capulin Basalt extending from road off to the right is the terminal pressure ridge of one flow. (0.6)

15.2 At 9:00 Triassic Chinle red beds are visible along the base of the slope. Dakota sandstone (brown, underlain by white Purgatoire Sandstone) still holds up the mesa rims. (0.2)

15.4 Gully exposing Baby Capulin Basalt. (1.0)

16.4 Lenticular sands of Chinle at 3:00. The Chinle Group was deposited on a broad floodplain dotted with lakes. (0.9)

17.3 On the left is the end of another of the long lava flows from Baby Capulin Mountain. Note Chinle "island" at 10:00 surrounded by basalt in the middle of the valley. (0.5)

17.8 Bridge. Thin-bedded, fine sand-

stones of Chinle red beds are exposed in the roadcut just ahead on the right. (1.0)

18.8 On the left, the line of big trees marks the absolute end of the lava flows. This point is about 22 miles from Baby Capulin volcano, the source of these flows. This long distance implies that they must have been very fluid, and erupted rapidly and in large quantity. Otherwise the lava would have frozen before it reached this far. (0.2)

19.0 Ranch Road enters on left. (Road goes to the Cross L Ranch House. At one time this ranch covered most of northeastern New Mexico.) At 3:00, below the red beds, is an old stone wall. (0.5)

19.5 Spur on mesa at right has a prominent ledge of white Purgatoire Sandstone under dark Dakota sandstone cap. (Entrada Sandstone on top of Chinle red beds at base of slope is not visible.) Morrison Formation, in between, is covered by landslide as usual. (0.5)

20.0 Bridge over the Dry Cimarron River. At 10:00 on middle of hillside is greenish-gray outcrop of Morrison shale. The top of the Chinle Group red beds is now lower down the canyon walls than it was a few miles back. (0.8)

20.8 Pavement ends. There are 17 miles of graded gravel road ahead. On south canyon slope (at 3:00 before making the sharp left turn) are the remains of an old stone wall. We know these walls were built before 1870 because they were marked on the original U.S. Government Land Office surveys made in the early 1870s. Ahead on far mesa edge is exceptionally thick Dakota sandstone rim. The Dakota sandstone rim ahead has a thin-bedded upper sandstone overlying the main cliff-forming sandstone. (0.2)

Remains of this stone wall at 20.8, built prior to 1870, are barely visible today.

21.0 Road ahead turns right beyond ranch house on left. (1.0)

22.0 MP 22. Gleason Canyon at 3:00. (1.0)

23.0 MP 23. A thick sequence of Chinle Group red beds is exposed on the left. The Entrada Sandstone is missing here, and the Chinle Group is overlain by a thin Morrison Formation, a small white cliff of Purgatoire Sandstone, and is capped by three cliff-forming beds of brown Dakota sandstone. (0.5)

23.5 Long Canyon Road enters on the left. (0.9)

24.4 Narrow bridge over Dry Cimarron River. Above the red beds at 9:00 is a thin white band of Entrada Sandstone. From here east, notice the progressive thickening of the Entrada Sandstone. Pastures here have healthy stands of the staghorn cholla cactus. (1.1)

25.5 To the left rear in the creek bottom are rapids over resistant sandstone in the lower Chinle red beds. (0.5)

26.0 MP 26. The boulder of Dakota sandstone on the knoll at 1:00 is locally known as Lizard Rock. (1.7)

27.7 STOP 4 - **Pavement begins again, briefly. Baldy Hill is ahead at 11:30.** It is capped by the Morrison Formation, and underlain by Entrada Sandstone (white band) and Chinle Group red beds. On left in valley are low benches held up by the bluish sands of the principal subdivision of the Chinle Group, the Travesser Formation. Below it are the oldest exposed beds in northeastern New Mexico, consisting of the Triassic Baldy Hill Formation.

North skyline is in Colorado. Seven L Buttes, a continuation of Mesa de Maya (with a Raton Basalt cap dated at 5.1 million years) is on the skyline at 10:00. Ahead and to the right is another Dakota-capped mesa. (0.3)

28.0 MP 28. Pavement ends. (2.0)

30.0 MP 30. Junction with NM-370 just ahead. (Turn right here up Travesser Canyon to begin Trip 3. Most of the next 37 miles on NM-370 are unpaved.)

Continuing along this trip down the Dry Cimarron River, you will reach pavement in 10 miles. Beyond this point on the left is a colorful hill called Steamboat Butte (sometimes called Battleship Mountain), with a prominent angular unconformity. The road ahead offers a brief view of Oklahoma followed by a climb onto the High Plains, and a crossing of the Santa Fe Trail on the way to Clayton. (1.0)

31.0 MP 31. For the next 2 miles, we will cross the Guy monocline, a gentle fold in the rocks that drops the far side down several hundred feet. The Guy monocline is a shallow, single-limbed fold with no more than 400 feet of relief. Nonetheless, it is one of the major structural features in this area. Like most of the structural features in this area, it is of Laramide age—that is to say, late Cretaceous to early Tertiary, and associated with the widespread deformation that took place during the Laramide orogeny.

To the right rear the brown silt part of the Morrison Formation, the Entrada Sandstone, and the underlying Travesser

Baldy Hill.

Formation make a small nose on the steep slope. (1.4)

32.4 Road bends to the left. Travesser Creek reaches southward. (0.3)

32.7 Cliff on left side of the road is held up by a cap of Entrada Sandstone that overlies the red beds of the Travesser Formation. (0.5)

33.2 To the left most of the bedrock is covered by landslide debris. (0.8)

34.0 MP 34. On the left, above road level, massive red beds of the Travesser Formation are overlain by a thin (less than 10 feet) section of Entrada Sandstone. (0.5)

Red beds of the Travesser Formation.

34.5 Ranch road to the right. Observe the variations in thickness of the Entrada Sandstone. At 9:00, the basalt flows rest on tilted beds of the Dakota Group. The Colorado- New Mexico state line is about where the Entrada Sandstone crops out at 9:00. (0.3)

34.8 Pavement begins again, briefly, for the next half mile or so. (0.2)

35.0 MP 35. Bridge across Dry Cimarron River. (0.2)

35.2 Pavement ends. (0.3)

35.5 Former location of Valley post office. At 9:00 red beds dip east. The Entrada Sandstone in the vicinity is only about 20 feet thick. Raton Basalt forms the high cliff on the left. (1.3)

36.8 Valley School was on the right. At 7:00 several flows of basalt cap the mesa, resting on the eroded surface of Dakota sandstone. Outcrops along the road ahead are Travesser Formation. (0.3)

37.1 At 9:00 the Travesser Formation tilts east under a (covered) unconformity beneath nearly flat-lying Entrada Sandstone. (0.3)

37.4 Pavement begins. (0.6)

38.0 MP 38. At 10:00 a clastic plug stands above the bench of red beds. We will see many more of these clastic plugs ahead, and an excellent cross section of one in a roadcut at mile 56.1 ahead. They are formed when the underlying layers of unconsolidated sediment are forced upward through the overlying rocks before any of them had time to become the hard, resistant units they are today.

The Entrada Sandstone is probably absent at the base of the main steep slope at

CLASTIC PLUGS AND SANDSTONE DIKES

Scattered throughout this part of New Mexico are a number of strange-looking cylindrical rock features that protrude from the landscape or are exposed in outcrop. Geologists refer to these features as clastic plugs. They range in size from 10 to 270 feet in diameter and consist of masses of broken rock debris surrounded by ring fractures. Clastic plugs are sometimes associated with enriched mineral deposits. Because of the mineralization associated with these structures, they are more resistant to erosion than the surrounding rocks and tend to stand in sharp relief to the surrounding landscape.

Clastic plugs form when underlying layers of unconsolidated sediment are forced upward through the overlying rocks. The highly brecciated nature of the rock within these plugs, along with other physical features like slickensides, are evidence of the upward movement of this material. Although "intrusive" in a mechanical sense—in that soft sediment can intrude upward into overlying strata—the structures themselves are not associated with igneous activity.

8:00. From 3:00 to 4:00 many clastic plugs dot the valley floor. (1.7)

39.7 Top of hill. Clastic plug on the left, at the base of a steep slope. The Entrada Sandstone is mostly covered by landslides. (0.8)

40.5 Top of hill. From 2:30 to 3:00, the Sheep Pen Sandstone forms the persistent ledge halfway up the side of the mesa. The orange-colored Entrada Sandstone appears to be absent in places above the Sheep Pen. At 9:00 the Entrada Sandstone rests on the Sloan Canyon Formation, the Sheep Pen Sandstone is absent. Here the valley of the Dry Cimarron River is very broad. (1.8)

42.3 Bridge across the Dry Cimarron River. Road curves left just ahead. To the south, the Sheep Pen Sandstone forms the 20-foot ledge on the bench that projects from the main mesa; the ledge is overlain by nearly 90 feet of sandstone that projects above the level of the lower brown, silty part of the Morrison; evidently this was a residual hill of Sheep Pen Sandstone that was not buried until after the lower brown, silty interval was deposited.

To the north, the west-dipping red beds of the Travesser Formation are on the west side of the pre-Entrada fold that resulted in the removal of the Sheep Pen and Sloan Canyon Formations over the anticline before the Entrada Sandstone was deposited over it. (1.7)

44.0 Entrada Sandstone thickens abruptly ahead. This marks the westernmost edge of the lower sandstone bed of the Entrada. (1.0)

45.0 On the right is a south-trending fault

that offsets the Entrada Sandstone about 40 feet. At 9:00 across the valley the Entrada rests on the red beds of the Travesser Formation. (0.7)

The fault here is evident in the 40-foot offset visible in the Entrada Sandstone cliff, downthrown to the left about 40 feet.

45.7 STOP 5 – Pull off on the right side of road. Steamboat Butte (also known as Battleship Mountain) is on the left side of the road just ahead. Note the tilted sandstone and red-brown mudstone of the Travesser Formation at the base of the mountain. The best view of this angular unconformity is about 0.2 miles ahead. (0.3)

Steamboat Butte. The underlying Triassic Travesser Formation was tilted and eroded before the overlying Jurassic Entrada Sandstone was deposited.

46.0 Wedding Cake Butte ahead, on the left side of the road. It is capped by the Morrison Formation; a lower brown, silty part of the Morrison forms the steeper slope

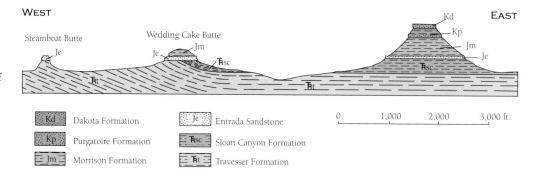

WEST

Steamboat Butte

Wedding Cake Butte

Kd

EAST

Kp

Jm

Je

Rsc

Rt

**Cross section of
Wedding Cake
Butte area.**

	Kd	Dakota Formation		Je	Entrada Sandstone
	Kp	Purgatoire Formation		Rsc	Sloan Canyon Formation
	Jm	Morrison Formation		Rt	Travesser Formation

0   1,000   2,000   3,000 ft.

**Wedding Cake
Butte. Slope of
Morrison
Formation at
top; double cliff
of Entrada
Sandstone over-
lies with a gen-
tle angular
unconformity
the red Sloan
Canyon
Formation and
(on the far side)
the Travesser
Formation.**

just above the white cliffs of the Entrada Sandstone. The Travesser Formation looks conformable with the overlying Entrada, but it is tilted to the east as seen on the cross section of this area. (1.2)

47.2 From 1:00 to 3:00 the massive white Entrada Sandstone at the base of the hillside overlies about 10 feet of thin-bedded Sheep Pen Sandstone. (0.8)

48.0 At 8:00 to 9:00 the small butte is the type locality for the Sheep Pen Sandstone. At the butte, the sandstone is 68 feet thick and rests on the Sloan Canyon Formation. Both the Sheep Pen Sandstone and the underlying Sloan Canyon Formation are cut out beneath the Entrada Sandstone by the pre- Entrada folding and erosion at Wedding Cake Butte. (1.2)

49.2 On either side of the road the Sloan Canyon forms low mesas. This is the type locality for the Sloan Canyon Formation of the Chinle Group. (0.8)

50.0 SLOW. Cross bridge over Sloan Canyon Creek and turn left. Just down-stream are sandstone dikes cutting the Sloan Canyon Formation. About 500 feet down-stream, the fossils remains of a phytosaur, a crocodile-like Triassic reptile, were collected. (0.8)

50.8 Clastic plug on left of road. Another plug on the right side of the road has been worked on a small scale for copper. The sur-rounding rock is the Sheep Pen Sandstone, which holds up the bench above the road to the right. (1.0)

51.8 Bridge. The clastic plug at 9:00 was reportedly mined for copper in the early 1900s. Development reportedly included a shaft 380 feet deep with several tunnels. The dark-brown knob at 1:30 is a clastic plug mineralized with the iron-rich mineral hematite. (0.5)

52.3 The low ridge at 3:00 is capped with the lower part of the Morrison Formation,

with the white Entrada Sandstone at the base. (0.6)

52.9 The knob on the left is capped with white sandstone, probably Sheep Pen. The mesa at 3:00 is capped by Dakota sandstone; the next sandstone down is Purgatoire, and the lower two sandstones are in the Morrison Formation. (0.7)

53.6 Goodson School on the left. In the hill behind it, part of the Morrison Formation and the underlying Entrada Sandstone are faulted down against the mudstones of the Sloan Canyon Formation, the knob to the left. (1.4)

55.0 Narrow bridge. The low bench at 4:00 is underlain by the Sloan Canyon Formation. (1.1)

56.1 STOP 6 on hilltop - The roadcut here provides a spectacular cross section through a clastic dike. Clastic dikes form

The remains of a phytosaur like the one seen here chasing a pack of *Coelophysis* were found in the Triassic Sloan Canyon Formation.

The clastic dike at Stop 6 intrudes the Sloan Canyon Formation and is capped by the younger Sheep Pen Sandstone.

THE GOODSON SCHOOL

The Felix E. Goodson Memorial School was built by the Works Progress Administration (WPA) of the federal government in 1936. It featured running water, flush toilets, a kitchen for hot lunches, and an auditorium. None of the three one-room schools in the valley that were consolidated into Goodson School had any of these amenities, only a stove for heating the classroom and outhouses at the edge of the schoolyard. The Goodson School closed in 1963; today it is unused and falling into ruin. Two of the one-room schools (Valley and New Mexico) have vanished altogether; all that remains of the third (Wagner) are the low stone walls.

Felix Goodson ranched in this area from 1926 to his death in the spring of 1936. In his later years he was county commissioner and lobbied strongly for this school. His wife, Stella, taught in the New Mexico School and took over the ranch operation after Felix's death. Their oldest daughter, LaVerne, married and moved into the Goodson ranch house, raising her family there. Raising cattle, growing alfalfa, gardening for food, surviving droughts, dust storms, hail storms, and sudden freezes, and raising children (and teaching them the social graces via dances and parties) required dedication and constant attention by both husband and wife.

LaVerne Hanners was one of five Goodson children. She wrote an evocative memoir, *Girl on a Pony*, that beautifully describes the challenges of trying to make a living in the valley during that era (see Suggested Reading).

when underlying layers of unconsolidated sediment are forced upward through the overlying rocks. Although "intrusive" in a mechanical sense—in that soft sediment can intrude upward into overlying strata—the structures themselves are not associated with igneous activity. Here the Sloan Canyon Sandstone is cut by the dike. The dike is capped with the Sheep Pen Sandstone. Note the many blocks of sandstone and mudstone that are tilted out of position. This disruption of bedding is one of the diagnostic features of a clastic dike. On the right side of the roadcut, at the east end, there is a later dike of light-gray sandstone. (0.9)

57.0 MP 57. Clastic plug forms a knob on the left side of the road. Note two more clastic plugs ahead on the right. At 9:00 in the slopes below the basalt-capped Black Mesa, the Dakota sandstone near the top and the Entrada Sandstone near the base are exposed fairly continuously; the remainder of the slopes are covered by talus and landslide debris. (0.7)

57.7 Clastic plugs on right. (0.2)

57.9 Junction of NM-456 and NM-406. The road straight ahead continues on to Kenton, Oklahoma. Kenton (3 miles from here) has a gas station. We turn right onto NM 406 to head to Clayton for Trip 1C. (0.1)

58.0 MP 35. End of Trip 1B

Junction of NM–456 & 406 to Clayton

Here the route turns south near the Oklahoma border and climbs out of the canyon of the Dry Cimarron River, heading south toward Clayton. It crosses rolling plains cut by the North Canadian and Cieneguilla (Seneca) Rivers and crosses the Santa Fe Trail near McNees Crossing. The divides between streams are capped by sands and gravels of the Ogallala Formation, the unit that holds up the High Plains of eastern Colorado, New Mexico, and the Texas Panhandle. Finally, as the route approaches Rabbit Ear Mountain, it crosses the easternmost edge of the Clayton-age lava flows. These basalts flowed onto the surface of the Ogallala Formation 2 to 3 million years ago.

0.0 Junction of NM-456 & NM-406. Reset odometer at MP 35. (1.0)

1.0 MP 34. Bridge across Carrizozo Creek. (1.1)

2.1 Remains of slush pit of the Pure Oil Mesa #2 oil test to the right of the road. No oil was found. On the left the Purgatoire Sandstone is exposed only at the left and right ends of the mesa below the Dakota sandstone cap. The sandstones exposed in the lower third of the slope are in the Morrison Formation. (0.6)

2.7 The butte on the left is capped with a thin sandstone at the top of the Purgatoire Formation; the shale member is covered, but the lower Purgatoire Sandstone is exposed half way down the side of the hill. (0.3)

3.0 MP 32. (0.2)

3.2 On the left the mesa is capped with Dakota sandstone; the sandstone member of the Purgatoire Formation is half way down the slope. It is overlain by a medium- to dark-gray shale member that is generally covered by debris from the overlying Dakota Group. (0.4)

3.6 Cattleguard. (0.2)

3.8 Morrison Formation in roadcut. (0.1)

3.9 Bridge across Road Canyon Creek. (0.2)

The roadcut at 4.1 exposes white sandstones and red shales of the Morrison Formation, overlain by Purgatoire Sandstone.

4.1 Highway curves left. The few feet of light-brown sandstone at the top of the roadcut is the bottom of the sandstone member of the Purgatoire Formation. It rests on light-gray siltstone and sandstone and greenish and maroon mudstone of the Morrison Formation. The thick sandstone at the lower end of the cut is part of the Morrison Formation. (0.3)

4.4 Top of the massive sandstone that is the basal, cliff-forming unit of the Dakota Group. The sandstone is well exposed as the rim rock on either side of the road. (0.2)

4.6 SLOW. Top of Rief Hill. Road turns right. Thin-bedded sandstone and shale of the Dakota Group in roadcuts. From here to Clayton the road is on either Dakota sandstone or the overlying veneer of river deposits derived from the Sangre de Cristo Mountains (the Ogallala Formation, the prime aquifer of this region and the Texas Panhandle), and, for a short distance, on the easternmost tongue of a Clayton-age basalt flow. (0.9)

5.5 The route is on the upper part of the Dakota Group, which here has been eroded into many small knobs. (0.5)

6.0 MP 29. (1.5)

7.5 Climb up onto Ogallala Formation from the Dakota Group; the Graneros Shale that covered the Dakota is absent here as a result of erosion before the deposition of the Ogallala Formation.

The widespread Ogallala Formation

THE MORRISON FORMATION

The Late Jurassic Morrison Formation was named for outcrops in the town of Morrison, near Denver, Colorado. It overlies the extensive sand dune deposits of the Entrada Sandstone that cover much of the Four Corner states. They are extremely thick (and perhaps best known) in Zion National Park, Utah. The most significant uranium deposits in New Mexico are found in sandstones of the Morrison Formation, near Grants.

The Morrison consists mainly of sluggish river and floodplain deposits that accumulated in an arid to semi-arid region. In the Dry Cimarron Valley exposures, the Morrison Formation ranges in thickness from 200 to more than 350 feet. Its mudstones are distinctive in having a variety of colors: light gray-green or gray red. The overlying Dakota Group mudstones are medium or dark gray. Mudstones dominate in the lower Morrison and white sandstones dominate in the upper. This upward-coarsening trend is the result of the approaching shoreline and associated lagoon, beach, and channel deposits of the overlying Dakota Group.

Nodular red-brown chalcedony forms a persistent and easily recognizable marker bed low in the Morrison. Usually referred to as the "agate bed," it is recognized over many of the southern Rocky Mountain states. It may represent an ancient soil developed on volcanic ash. An excellent exposure is in the roadcut by the pipeline at Mile 5.5, Trip 3.

Late Jurassic paleogeography of the southwestern U.S.

holds up the High Plains east of the Rocky Mountains. The plains used to be connected to the Rockies; they are the floodplains of the numerous rivers that drained east from them. Since then rivers such as the Pecos and Canadian in New Mexico have grown northward and cut off the connection between the mountains and their floodplain. The rivers of Colorado have done the same. The western extent of the Ogallala in our area is preserved under the Raton-age basalts above Raton. The Clayton-age flows follow drainages that are incised into the Ogallala surface. The stored groundwater in this formation that is now isolated from its source constitutes the lifeblood of the pivot-irrigation systems upon which agriculture on the High Plains is totally dependent.

Most of the uplands in eastern Union County are held up by the Ogallala Formation. The Clayton-age basalt flows preserve the valleys that mark the beginning of the dissection of the Ogallala surface. Much of that residual surface is capped by a thick caliche layer, the caprock of the Texas High Plains. (1.5)

9.0 MP 26. At 3:00 the bare benches a mile to the west are on the top of the Dakota Group. (0.4)

9.4 "Dead" windmill on left. The gently rolling surface we are crossing is cut into the unconsolidated sands and gravels of the Ogallala Formation. (0.8)

10.2 Rabbit Ear Mountain at 11:30; Sierra Grande at 2:00. (0.1)

10.3 Cattleguard. Route follows a ridge that is capped by the Ogallala Formation.

Sandstone of the Dakota Group is exposed in the valleys on either side; the Graneros Shale, which here lies between the Dakota and Ogallala Formations, is mostly covered. (1.6)

11.9 Cattleguard. The shrub-covered mesas on the right are capped with sandstones of the Dakota Group. The ridge along the route is formed by the Ogallala Formation. (0.8)

12.7 Cattleguard. (0.7)

13.4 Curve right. Junction with NM-410 on the left. The Santa Fe Trail extends northeast through the intersection. (0.6)

14.0 MP 21. (0.7)

Rabbit Ear Mountain, in an early postcard view from the outskirts of Clayton.

14.7 Moses store and gas station (closed). Curve left. The highway is now back on the Ogallala Formation; the contact with the underlying Dakota Group is a few hundred feet south of the store. (0.7)

15.4 The gully at the left side of the curve is the result of the heavy traffic over the Santa Fe Trail. (0.4)

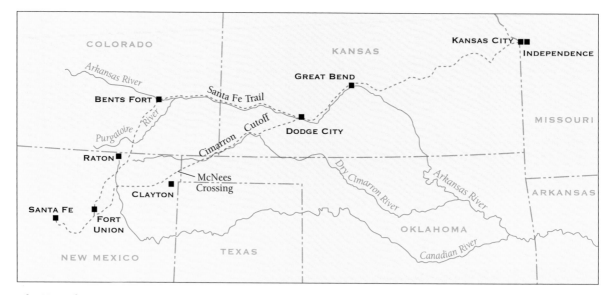

The 230-mile journey on the Santa Fe Trail from Missouri to New Mexico took most travelers over a month.

15.8 Narrow bridge across the North Canadian River (Corrumpa Creek). The massive sandstone is in the upper part of the Dakota Group. Highway ascends hill. The roadcut ahead is in the thin-bedded sandstone and siltstone of the upper part of the Dakota Group. The dark-gray beds are plant-bearing coaly shales. (0.7)

16.5 STOP 1 – Pull over and park at historical marker for McNees Crossing. The site is named for two young men, McNees and Monroe, who were shot at this crossing on the Santa Fe Trail in 1828. McNees and Monroe went ahead of their caravan and stopped to bathe then took a nap at the crossing of Corrumpa Creek, a

Arrival of the Caravan at Santa Fe, from the 1844 edition of Josiah Gregg's *Commerce of the Prairies.*

branch of the North Canadian River. Indians stole their guns and shot them. McNees died here; Monroe was carried on by his caravan but died en route. He was buried on the Cimarron. Soon after, six or seven Indians showed up and were shot down by vengeful traders. One Indian got away. This incident sparked the outrages on the trail that led to the first military escort in 1829. Following this event traders on the Santa Fe Trail called Corrumpa Creek "McNees Creek." (Corrumpa is an Indian word meaning wild, or isolated.)

At 8:00, a mile away, is a white pillar in front of a steep bank at McNees Crossing. This monument to the days of the Santa Fe Trail was installed in 1921. The monument is on private land, just this side of Corrumpa Creek. You are welcome to walk to the monument, but please close the gate behind you. Original trail ruts can still be seen faintly near the crossing. Here, too, a group of travelers celebrated Independence Day in 1831, the first documented 4th of July observed on the plains.

The Cimarron Cutoff of the Santa Fe Trail was first used about 1822; it saved many miles because the main trail went west to the base of the mountains following the Arkansas River and then south across Raton Pass (see map); however, the Cimarron route had water holes spaced as much as 30 miles apart; this meant several dry camps. Fort Union, now a national monument, was built in 1851 at the junction of the two routes to afford protection from Indian raids. (0.3)

16.8 The old Moses Church is in the valley to the right. Hill beyond rises westward on a surface sloped on the Dakota Group;

Graneros Shale is exposed on this side of the valley. In roadcut is the slabby, felted limestone of the Graneros Shale. It lies about 15 feet above the highest sandstone of the Dakota Group and is characterized by tiny needles of calcite shell fragments. The scar just above the flat at 4:00 is a remnant of the Santa Fe Trail. (0.2)

19.0 MP 16. Rabbit Ear Mountain is visible on the horizon at 2:00. (1.0)

20.0 MP 15 at west end of curve. (2.0)

22.0 The base of the Ogallala Formation is about at road level. The highway, even with all its bends, is following section lines. (0.7)

22.7 SLOW. Highway turns left. Junction with Campbell Road on right. A short detour down Campbell Road (about 4 miles one way) will bring you to another crossing of the Santa Fe Trail and an interpretive site on the Kiowa National Grasslands. (1.1)

23.8 Seneca School on left. (0.2)

Low aerial view of McNees Crossing, where the Cimarron Cutoff of the Santa Fe Trail crosses Corrumpa Creek, just west of the New Mexico-Oklahoma border. View is to the southwest, with ruts of the Santa Fe Trail clearly visible beyond the cut in the stream bank. The monument was erected in 1921.

24.0 MP 11. (3.3)

27.3 Bridge across Cieneguilla Creek (commonly called Seneca Creek). (0.7)

28.0 MP 7. On left an irrigation well was drilled that yielded 1,000 gallons of water per minute from sand and gravel of the Ogallala Formation. (1.0)

29.0 MP 6. We are now driving on a basalt flow that covers the Ogallala Formation. This flow ends 1.3 miles to the east. The identical nature of this flow to the one under the town of Clayton, and to the broad bench extending west under the younger volcanic cones of Rabbit Ear and Mt. Dora (sometimes known as Cieneguilla del Burro) suggests that the source for this large basalt blanket is near Sierra Grande, nearly 40 miles to the west. (0.5)

29.5 Descend from ridge. Roadcut on right shows basalt resting on sandy clay of the Ogallala Formation, the upper foot of which is here turned to a brick-red color because of baking by the lava flow. Ahead on the right are cattle feed lots. (2.1)

31.6 NM-411 enters on left. (3.4)

35.0 Junction with US-64. Turn right toward the city of Clayton. (1.2)

36.2 Ascend hill leaving the poorly consolidated tan sandy clay and gravel of the Ogallala Formation and climbing onto the Clayton-age basalt flow that extends west to the neighborhood of Sierra Grande, visible at 2:00. (1.0)

37.2 Rabbit Ear Mountain, one of about 80 extinct volcanoes in Union County, is at 2:00. Its distinctive shape was a prominent landmark along the Cimarron Cutoff of the Santa Fe Trail. The round-topped butte just to the right of Rabbit Ear Mountain and the low double hill at 3:00 are also extinct volcanoes. The three volcanoes are in a line that trends northwest. (0.5)

37.7 Intersection of US-64 and US-87 in downtown Clayton. End of Trip 1C. For the history of Clayton, see Trip 4, which travels US-64/87 from Clayton to Raton.

SCENIC TRIP TWO - (22 MILES)
Des Moines to Capulin Via Folsom on NM–325

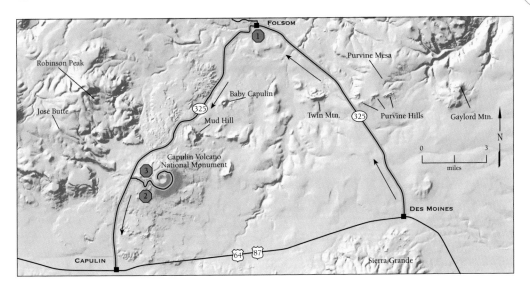

The route skirts the well-preserved cinder cones of Twin Mountain, Baby Capulin, and Capulin Mountain, as well as many older volcanoes from Des Moines to Folsom and on to Capulin Volcano National Monument on the west side of the peak. The trip follows the spiral road to the crater rim of Capulin Mountain, which offers a view that encompasses all of northeastern New Mexico as well as parts of Texas, Oklahoma, and Colorado. The deep crater of Capulin Mountain can also be seen from the parking lot on the crater rim. Returning from the crest to the junction of the monument road and NM-325, the trip continues into the village of Capulin where it rejoins US 64/87. Altitudes along the route vary from a low of about 6,400 feet at the town of Folsom to 8,215 feet on the rim trail of Capulin Mountain.

Only limited exposures of older rocks are seen on this route. These include the Cretaceous Dakota Group sandstones and the Purgatoire Formation, and the Jurassic Morrison Formation. Most of the trip is on various basaltic flows of the quite recent sequence known as the Capulin-age basalts. Many features of lava flows and volcanoes can be seen on this route. Also seen are some of the Clayton-age volcanoes and Raton-age flows, the latter being the older.

0.0 Log starts at the junction of NM-325 and US-64/87 on the west side of Des Moines. Travel north on NM-325. (0.3)

0.3 Cross Colorado and Southern Railway. Contour ridges in valley on right are to prevent soil erosion by runoff from torrential summer rains. To the right in the distance is Dunchee Hill, the eroded remnant of a Clayton-age volcano. (1.4)

1.7 MP 15. The road to the left leads to a former carbon dioxide compressor plant. We are now over the Des Moines field, an exhausted carbon dioxide field. Gas from this field was compressed and shipped from 1955 through 1966 for use as a refrigerant in long distance refrigerated trucks. Other carbon dioxide fields are still producing south of Clayton, including the giant Bravo Dome field, with an estimated reserve of 10 to 16 trillion cubic feet of gas. Gas produced from Bravo Dome is used for re-pressurizing aging oil and gas fields in the Permian Basin (of west Texas and southeastern New Mexico), to coax more oil and gas from the pore spaces in the reservoir rocks.

On the left, Capulin Mountain looms on the horizon; the diagonal scar on the side is the road to the crater rim. Other peaks visible beyond and to the right of Capulin Mountain are José Butte and Robinson Peak (farthest to the right). (0.3)

2.0 Gaylord Mountain, another Clayton-age volcano, is on the skyline to the right. Material for this road came from pits on the north side of Gaylord Mountain. Road curves left. About 2 miles straight ahead on the skyline are three elongate ridges; these are the fissure vents of the Purvine Hills. These fissures and Twin Mountain, to the left of the highway at 11:00, are on a line and have identical compositions. They probably all erupted simultaneously.

On the distant skyline, in the gap between the middle and right vents of the Purvine Hills fissures, is Emery Peak (7,350 feet), a Clayton-age volcano that is the key to the volcanic history of the region because basalt from it flowed down into the Dry Cimarron River and dammed it. Basalt from other Clayton-age volcanoes as well as the much younger Capulin-age sequences flowed into the lake that formed behind the basalt dam. Emery Peak and East Emery Peak (behind the right fissure of the Purvine Hills) rest on a Raton Basalt cap that extends eastward (forested skyline ridge) behind Gaylord Mountain. (0.5)

2.5 On the left is the highest point on the Colorado and Southern Railway between Denver, Colorado and Fort Worth, Texas. At 6,678 feet above sea level, you are now higher than downtown Raton, Trinidad, Walsenburg, Colorado Springs, and Denver. (0.2)

2.7 MP 14. (0.5)

3.2 Purvine Hills fissure volcanoes on skyline between 12:30 and 2:30. Their elongate shape is evident from here. (0.2)

3.4 Ranch road enters on right. Between 7:00 and 11:00 to the left at least 14 volcanoes (each mountain peak) can be seen. (0.6)

4.0 Crossing basalt from the westernmost Purvine Hills fissure (red hill at 3:00). The flow moved toward Twin Mountain (at 11:00 with large cinder pit that has nearly eliminated the north flank), buried the near edge of the cone and then flowed northward into the Dry Cimarron River east of Folsom. (0.5)

4.5 Twin Mountain is now directly on your left. The source of the lava was in the groove (you're looking along it) between the two flanks of the cone. The cinders are being hauled away for railroad ballast by the Colorado and Southern Railway and are being used to make concrete cinder blocks for houses, acoustical insulation, etc. (0.2)

4.7 MP 12. Roadcuts are in the upper part of the Cretaceous Dakota Group. The Dakota forms the upper mesa edge to the right as well as the mesa margin down the Dry Cimarron Canyon into Oklahoma. (0.3)

5.0 Road enters on left from Colorado and Southern Railway cinder pit on Twin Mountain. The red color of some of the mountain is iron oxide (rusty iron) stains in the cinders. The flat surface ahead for the next mile or so is underlain by basalt from Twin Mountain. At right, just beyond old road, are Purvine Hills basalt outcrops. On the left nearly a mile away is a low ridge, a volcano called Augite Vent after its characteristic mineral, augite, which stands out in relief as little tablets on weathered surfaces. It is a Clayton-age vent that flowed into the lake behind the Emery Peak Basalt dam. (1.0)

6.0 Outcrops of Twin Mountain Basalt on both sides of the road. The entire skyline ahead is Johnson Mesa (in distance at 11:00) and Oak Canyon Mesa (11:30 to 2:00), which are capped by the earlier sequence of Raton basalts that extends westward to Raton. The cliff-forming basalt under Emery Peak (3:00) is the continuation of this Raton Basalt cap. (0.3)

6.3 Stream between walls of basalt from Baby Capulin, the small bare mountain on your left just to the right and in front of tree-covered Mud Hill, which in turn is to right and in front of Capulin Mountain (on skyline with road circling up it).

Both the Fort Union-Fort Dodge military wagon road of Santa Fe Trail days and the later Goodnight-Loving Trail passed across this flat. In the middle distance at 1:00 is Big Hill, a Clayton-age volcano that erupted at the same time as Emery Peak volcano.

Twin Mountain fissure vent. The original shape was of two parallel ridges of cinders with a trough between, from which the cinders were erupted.

Capulin Mountain. Mud Hill is just to the right.

We're off the edge of Baby Capulin Basalt just ahead; roadcuts here are in the uppermost Morrison Formation. The Dry Cimarron River valley is ahead. Buffalo Head, a Raton Basalt-capped butte, is on skyline ahead.(0.6)

6.9 Roadcuts in uppermost Morrison Formation. (0.3)

7.2 Railroad cuts at left in uppermost Morrison Formation and basal Purgatoire Formation. Ridge behind is capped by Dakota sandstone. (0.1)

7.3 STOP 1 - Entering the village of Folsom; junction with NM-456. (Trip 1B down Dry Cimarron Canyon begins in the center of town at the Folsom Museum. NM-72 from here heads west to Raton.) Pull over and park at the Folsom Museum.

Folsom is a small village in the valley of the Dry Cimarron River. When the Denver, Texas & Fort Worth Railroad was completed in 1888, it gave the construction camp of Ragtown new life. It was renamed Folsom in honor of Frances Folsom, who had married President Cleveland in the White House in 1886. The town became the only source of medicine, ranch supplies, groceries, and

clothing, and wagons came from 100 miles away. In the late 1800s, after the Plains Indians were forced onto reservations, Folsom became an important cattle drive route. Ranchers homesteaded around Capulin, and the Goodnight Loving Trail passed nearby. Charles Goodnight had trailed many herds of cattle from Texas to Wyoming from 1866 to 1869 and used this route instead of Raton Pass; it was an easier grade and he felt the Wooten toll was too costly. Folsom was once the largest cattle-shipping center west of Fort Worth, Texas.

By 1895 it had two mercantile stores, three saloons, and other businesses. It also was contributing to the outlaw history of New Mexico. Thomas E. "Black Jack" Ketchum, the leader of an infamous gang who was wounded after robbing a train near Folsom, was treated at the Folsom Hotel. He was tried in Clayton, New Mexico and hung. The town prospered for a while as a stockyard and shipping center until the 1908 flood.

At the beginning of the summer of 1954 two of the authors, Sally and Bill Muehlberger, and their two-year-old, Karen, moved their household to Folsom, New Mexico for two months of geologic field

The Folsom Hotel, built in 1888. Black Jack Ketchum was treated for his wounds here before being taken to Clayton for trial.

Doherty Mercantile, built in 1896, today houses the Folsom Museum.

work. They were accompanied by field assistant Gordon Adams. "Upon arrival we found a house on the main street that was perfect, except for the fact that it was sealed into two parts. We heard that two spinster sisters who lived there previously had stopped speaking, and they had built a wall to partition the house to ensure each other's privacy. We remedied that immediately. There was a windmill in the backyard that had to be turned on to get water. This involved wading through high grass, which we were told housed a bull snake—harmless to us but good for rodents, so we left it alone. We rented a washing machine with a wringer from the town's garage on Main street. It had been used to wash rags. We rented a used refrigerator in Clayton, and a set of practical Melmac plastic dishes in Trinidad."

The friendliness of the people made the summer very enjoyable. The trip to the general store that housed the post office was a daily highlight. Sally was invited to meetings of the garden club at the Purvine Ranch. Years later Sally, whose maiden name was Provine, learned the name was part of her geneology. On July 4th they attended a barbeque on the Burchard Ranch, 20 miles down the Dry Cimarron River. "We heard the river would flood later in the day, so we took a *before* picture. The flash flood didn't materialize until 10 o'clock that night! There was, needless to say, no *after* picture."

Continue straight ahead on NM-325 on this trip to Capulin Mountain and the town of Capulin. (0.4)

7.7 MP 9. Road turns sharp left. (0.1)

7.8 Cross tracks of Colorado and Southern Railway. (0.1)

7.9 Road turns sharp right. (0.2)

8.1 Embankment on right is for flood protection. On west side (far) side of flood channel is the end of the basalt flow that moved north from Capulin Mountain. (0.1)

8.2 Purgatoire Sandstone is exposed in roadcut on right. Capulin Mountain at 11:00. At 2:00 on skyline is José Butte, the last

THE CAPULIN HOTEL

The altitude of 6,400 feet gave Folsom an ideal year-round climate. In the 1880s plans were made to build an elegant spa that would rival Colorado Springs. The many-turreted Capulin Hotel was built. There were one hundred rooms; each contained a fireplace and papered walls. The river was dammed to create a lake for boating. The hotel was nearly finished when the builders had a disagreement and left, leaving no money or anyone in charge, and so the building was abandoned. Families moved in while they built their own homes, then started using the hotel parts for themselves. The building itself washed away in the 1908 flood.

Clayton-age volcano to pour lava into the lake behind the Emery Peak lava dam. (0.3)

8.5 Road begins climb over Dakota sandstone rim. (0.3)

Baby Capulin Mountain, the youngest volcano in this region.

8.8 Road curves left past corner of Folsom cemetery. Here a large dark granite boulder with a bronze plaque reads:

In honored memory of Sarah J. Rooke, telephone operator, who perished in the flood waters of the Dry Cimarron at Folsom, New Mexico, August 27, 1908, while at her switchboard warning others of danger. With heroic devotion she glorified her calling by sacrificing her own life that others might live. "Greater love hath no man than this." Erected by her fellow workers.

The road to the right goes to the Cornay Ranch. (0.2)

9.0 Baby Capulin, the most recent volcano in this region, is straight ahead. The road drops off the Dakota sandstone rim into a valley flanked by basalt from tree-covered Capulin Mountain on right and Baby Capulin on left. Sierra Grande, (8,720 feet), the largest volcano in northeastern New Mexico, is prominent on the horizon at 11:00. (0.7)

9.7 MP 7. The road turns right, paralleling the edge of Baby Capulin basalt. (0.8)

10.5 Baby Capulin is on the left. It is an excellent example of a cinder cone. Test pits at right edge were made to determine the quality of cinders for road foundations, etc. Near the small juniper bushes in the middle ground lava from Baby Capulin flowed over the edge of Capulin Mountain lava, indicating that Baby Capulin is younger. Down the Dry Cimarron Valley from Folsom, Baby Capulin lava rests on Twin Mountain-Purvine Hills-type lava. Baby Capulin is

SARAH ROOKE

Sarah (Sally) Rooke came to Folsom from Iowa in 1905 when she was 65, and became an operator at the Folsom Telephone Exchange. People still speak of her heroism on a night in August 1908, when she heard a buzz on her switchboard and was told "The river has broken loose. Run for your life!" She realized that many people were unaware of the danger and called them, one by one, until she was swept away by the flood. Her body was found several miles below Folsom. A news article told of her unmarked grave, and coworkers throughout the United States, some not even with her telephone company, contributed a dime apiece to erect a granite and bronze tablet for her monument. It bore a tribute from 4,324 coworkers, some from as far away as New York. The flood took 17 lives and destroyed most of the downtown businesses, most of which were never rebuilt. Today there is a post office, ruins of the old general store, the Folsom Hotel, gas station, and the Folsom Museum (formerly Doherty Mercantile).

thus the youngest of the volcanoes in this region. A few other vents are of this youngest cycle of eruptions (Capulin-age basalts), but their position in the sequence has not been determined, because broad areas of alluvial cover separate these outlying vents from the sequence seen in this region. (0.3)

10.8 Mud Hill is straight ahead. Layers of cinders in its walls can be seen. It must have been violent in its eruption, because most of this side is missing, presumably blown away. This valley was once covered with Mud Hill basalt, as is evident from the remnant preserved on the tiny butte in the valley on the right. It was eroded away, however, before the eruption of Capulin Mountain. Basalt from Capulin Mountain on left ahead and to right. José Butte is on the skyline at 2:30. (0.4)

11.2 Road climbs onto Capulin Mountain basalt. We will drive on top of this basalt until we're less than a mile from US 64/87 in the village of Capulin. Extending left from Mud Hill just ahead is a series of hills along a fissure volcano (the Great Wall). Some of the lava from this fissure caps the low mesas in the middle distance at 9:00. (0.3)

11.5 Road skirts base of Mud Hill. (0.2)

11.7 MP 5. Capulin Mountain is straight ahead. (0.5)

12.2 The low open side of Mud Hill where the lava poured out is visible to the left rear at 8:00. The hump near the right base of Capulin Mountain is a minor vent of pasty lava from the volcano. Nearly all of the liquid lava flowed out from a vent behind the flat-topped ridge to the right of the hump. Capulin Mountain itself is where the gases escaped, throwing lava into the air in small pieces that solidified by the time they landed on the cone. We are still driving on lava from Capulin Mountain. (0.4)

12.6 Cattleguard. Robinson Peak at 2:30 on Raton Basalt cap. (0.4)

13.0 Beside road on right are four round balls of lava called "squeeze-ups." They formed when the top of the lava flow solidified and cracked, allowing the pasty lava

Stratified pyroclastic material (bombs, cinders, ash) on the north flank of Mud Hill.

"Squeeze-ups" on the west side of highway 325, just north of the turnoff to Capulin Volcano National Monument.

below to squeeze up through the cracks like toothpaste. (0.1)

13.1 Road to Cornay Ranch enters on right. On left, about 100 yards from the road, is a brush- and tree-covered wall of basalt. Behind it was the pool of lava that poured through cracks in the wall to make the big flows we have been driving on.

Basalt from Capulin Mountain extends to the far edge of the valley on the right. Basalt cliffs rimming the side of the valley are Raton Basalts of the earliest sequence. Robinson Peak on the skyline at 3:00 and

José Butte at 2:30 are both Clayton-age volcanoes. (0.6)

13.7 We are now 7,200 feet above sea level. We have climbed 450 feet since the road started up the Capulin Mountain lava. Many volcanoes are visible ahead: Horseshoe Mountain at 11:45 (Capulin-age; barren; grooves down it); Palo Blanco Mountain (behind it on right); Timber Buttes at 12:30; Laughlin Peak (8,820 feet) at 1 (all Clayton-age); Larga Mesa at 2:00 (Raton-age). The village of Capulin at 11:00 is 6,868 feet above sea level. (0.2)

This detailed map shows the four major lava flows associated with Capulin Mountain. Coming south from Folsom we drove across the fourth (and last) episode, then onto the third episode. Just past the Visitor Center en route to the summit we drive between the lava levees of the second episode.

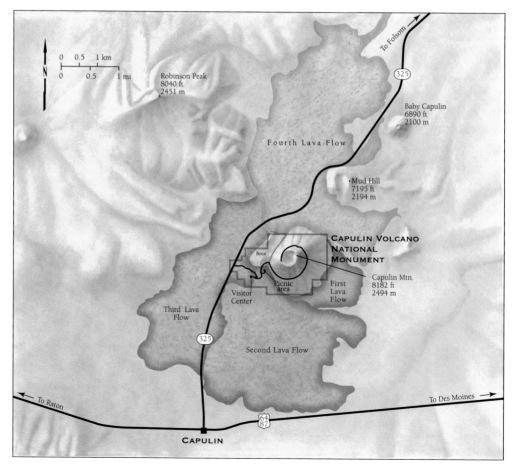

13.9 Turn left onto road for Capulin Volcano National Monument and the crater rim. The round trip to the crater rim from here is 5.4 miles. (0.1)

14.0 Road turns sharp right, then left. Tree-covered ridge at left is the outer wall of the former lava pool. Basalt lava broke through this wall and flowed down the slopes to the valleys below. (0.2)

14.2 Road turns sharp right. On left is grassy valley flanked with walls of basalt. These walls are the natural levees for the lava that poured out of the big central vent, known to geologists as "bocas" (Spanish for "mouth"). (0.1)

14.3 STOP 2 - **Capulin Volcano National Monument Visitor Center. Stop and pay entrance fee inside.** The monument was established in 1916 by presidential proclamation (Woodrow Wilson) and is under the jurisdiction of the National Park Service, US Department of the Interior. The small visitor center has excellent displays, a small bookstore, information, and restrooms.

Capulin Mountain was named for the Spanish word for chokecherries (capulin) that once were found around the mountain and now are found in the crater. Capulin National Monument was established in 1916, and the name was changed to Capulin Volcano National Monument in 1987. Activities include picnicking, bird watching, and hiking. A 2-mile road spirals up the volcano to the crater rim. In the 1920s a mule-drawn plow was used to grade this road to the rim. At the top the self-guided Crater Rim Trail offers great views of the surrounding countryside. By walking the trail you can become acquainted with the vegetation and wildlife. And if you have ever wanted to walk into a volcano, Capulin Mountain is one of the few places you can do it; there is a 0.2-mile-long trail that goes to the vent at the bottom of the crater. On a clear day you can see much of northeastern New Mexico and three other states from the 8,182 foot summit.

Today piñon pine, ponderosa pine, scrub oak, mountain mahogany, and juniper provide the vegetation. Deer, wild turkey, squirrels, and jays eat acorns from the scrub oak. In spring and early summer there are many wildflowers along the two trails, as well as many songbirds. Swarms of thousands of ladybugs appear on the rocks and plants in late summer. The chokecherry is a shrubby member of the rose family (the fruits make excellent jelly and syrup), and its late summer red berries have a sour bite, hence its name. There are mule deer, bob cats, antelope, coyotes, elk, mountain lion, and black bear. Red tailed hawks and American kestrels are here in summer, and in the fall mountain bluebirds appear.

Continue on road to summit. (0.1)

14.4 Road turns left through natural levee. (0.1)

14.5 Road to right goes to picnic area and restrooms. Picnic area is between the natural levees of the flow that moved south from here toward the village of Capulin. (0.1)

14.6 Bare hill ahead is the vent for lava from Capulin Mountain. Capulin Mountain itself was the escape hatch for gases that blew the lava into the air as fragments. The fragments then solidified in the air, although

Sierra Grande, at an elevation of 8,720 feet, is the highest and largest volcano in northeastern New Mexico.

they were still red hot when they landed on the cone. Just ahead the road turns right, passing end of natural levee. The road then skirts the lava vent on the left and natural levee on right and begins the spiral climb up Capulin Mountain. Please drive carefully. No passing is allowed on the paved volcano road. The road trip and view from here to the top will probably be enjoyed most by the passengers. (0.4)

Pressure ridges on Capulin Mountain basalt flow, looking south from the road to the summit.

15.0 At 1:30 on skyline is a Capulin-age volcano called Malpie Mountain (or Mount Marcy). To the left of it and on the distant

skyline are the Don Carlos Hills, a string of 14 Clayton-age volcanoes. (0.1)

15.1 All the area between us and Capulin village is covered with basalt from Capulin Mountain. (0.1)

15.2 Lava flow beyond the base of Capulin Mountain has prominent pressure ridges. These are formed when the upper surface gets stiff while the liquid lava below keeps moving and folds the upper part. Asphalt forms similar ridges as it slides off the high central parts of a highway. (0.1)

15.3 Sierra Grande at 1:30. Outer edges of Capulin Mountain basalt, about one mile out, are marked by lines of bushes. (0.4)

15.7 Village of Des Moines can be seen at the base of Sierra Grande (on the left). On a clear day over the edge of Sierra Grande, Rabbit Ear Mountain (5,940 feet) can be seen 40 miles away and north of Clayton. (0.1)

15.8 Pullout. This is an excellent place to stop and see bombs (black) encased in the cinders on the flank of the cinder cone. Each layer represents a "poof" of the eruption process. These cinders and bombs rained down on the cone and built it up just as you build a sand pile by letting sand trickle through your fingers. Ahead are more opportunities to see the layering of the cone. (0.1)

15.9 At 3:00 about 5 miles away, with red and black scars, is Twin Mountain, a volcano younger than Capulin Mountain. (0.1)

16.0 The big volcano about one mile north of us (with trees on far side) is Mud Hill, a Clayton-age volcano. Behind it another mile is Baby Capulin Mountain (bare cone into whose crater we can see). Baby Capulin is the youngest volcano in this region. Two miles beyond and slightly to the left is the village of Folsom. On the skyline to the north are broad mesas capped by the earlier Raton basalt sequence. Tree-covered flats, beyond road below us and extending nearly to Folsom, are underlain by basalt from Capulin Mountain. (0.1)

16.1 Robinson Peak, the cone with shoulder humps on both sides, is a Clayton-age

Baby Capulin.

volcano about 4 miles to west-northwest. (0.1)

16.2 José Butte is a Clayton-age volcano about 5 miles to the west. (0.3)

16.5 STOP 3 - Parking area, altitude 7,877 feet. Highest point on the other side of the rim is 8,215 feet. The panoramic sketch that follows identifies the major physiographic features that can be seen to the west. Below the viewpoint, near the base of Capulin Mountain, is the vent out of which the basalt lava flowed. The tree-covered rim that surrounds the vent is part of the wall that formerly enclosed the lava pool.

Turning around, we can look into the crater from which the gases escaped and blew the molten lava into the air, where it cooled, and dropped back to build up the present cone. The rim is higher on the other side because it was the downwind side during the eruption. The crater bottom is about 415 feet below the highest point on the rim.

A trail around the rim of the crater gives spectacular views in all directions as

Layers of volcanic cinders and bombs are exposed on the road to the summit. Thin layers of ash separate the cinder layers.

well as an opportunity to see wildlife, birds, and the piñon pines of the high rim. Another trail leads to the floor of the crater. Both trails are fairly short and are well worth the walk.

Retrace route to junction of monument road and NM-325. (2.5)

19.0 Turn left at junction of monument road and NM-325. (0.1)

19.1 Road begins a 400-foot descent to Capulin village. We'll be on top of Capulin Mountain lava for nearly the entire distance. Pullout on left is a good place for a photo panorama.(0.3)

19.4 Cattleguard. Road drops off the end of one lava flow onto the one under it. (0.3)

19.7 Horseshoe Mountain on skyline ahead is another Capulin-age volcano. Humps around base are basalt lava masses. (1.1)

20.8 The valley on our right drained east (left), somewhere under us, before Capulin Mountain erupted and stopped the drainage. The valley to the right is now a closed basin, the Capulin basin, containing large amounts of artesian water. Some of the water trapped in this basin, percolates through the cracks in the lava flows and emerges as springs near the southeastern base of Capulin Mountain. (0.4)

21.2 We have now driven off the end of the Capulin Mountain basalt. The southern rim of lava can be seen as brush-covered knobs on the left and right. (0.4)

21.6 Cattleguard. (0.2)

21.8 The village of Capulin, and junction with US 64/87. End of Trip 2.

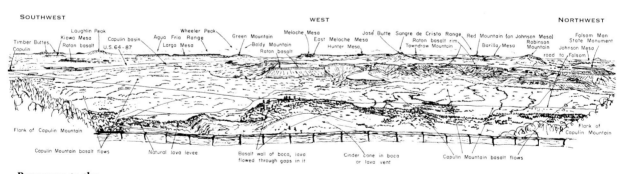

Panorama to the west from the rim of Capulin Mountain.

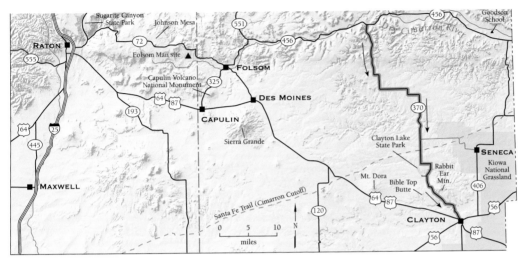

Dry Cimarron River to Clayton via NM–370

This trip begins at the junction of NM-456 and NM-370. The (largely unpaved) road climbs up Travesser Canyon on to the rolling High Plains. NM-370 intersects the road to Clayton Lake State Park, where hundreds of dinosaur footprints are exposed in the spillway of the dam. The trip continues on to Clayton.

0.0 Log begins at intersection of NM-456 and NM-370. Reset odometer to zero. Go south on NM-370. (0.5)

0.5 MP 47. (0.5)

1.0 At 3:00 the best continuous exposures of the section from the Entrada Sandstone up to the Dakota Group can be seen in this face. In this vicinity, the Travesser Formation has its type locality but is only 250 feet

thick, whereas it is commonly more than 400 feet thick. The yellow band is the Entrada Sandstone; the white immediately above is a gypsum cement in the lower part of the Morrison Formation and in the upper few feet of the Entrada Sandstone. Straight ahead the Dakota sandstone on the skyline

View to the west at mile 1.0. Red Travesser Formation capped by cliff-forming yellowish Entrada Sandstone. Above it (mostly covered) is the Morrison Formation.

is on the west, or upper side of the Guy monocline. (0.5)

1.5 MP 46. (0.6)

2.1 Cattleguard. The Dakota sandstone from 9:00 to 1:00 is on the Guy monocline. The Guy monocline is a shallow, single-limbed fold with only a few hundred feet of relief. Like most of the structural features in this area, it is of Laramide age—that is to say, late Cretaceous to early Tertiary, and associated with the widespread deformation that took place during the Laramide orogeny. (1.6)

3.7 Cattleguard. (0.1)

3.8 Bridge over Travesser Creek. (0.7)

4.5 MP 43. (0.1)

4.6 Chapman road to right. Pavement begins just ahead. (0.8)

5.4 Pipeline crossing above the first switchback; the pipeline is part of the abandoned Colorado Interstate Gas Company's line from Texas. Pieces of red-orange agate are sometimes strewn along the road, having fallen from the outcrop. The agate consists of chalcedony and calcite and breaks apart readily. The agate bed of the Morrison Formation has been recognized in much of the Rocky Mountain region and the western Plains. It may represent an ancient soil developed in volcanic ash. Continue up the hill; the Morrison Formation is thin bedded and in the upper part is maroon. (0.2)

5.6 Top of hill; pavement ends. The route is on the west, upper side of the Guy mono-

cline; the Dakota sandstone on the left dips eastward. (0.8)

6.4 Cattleguard. Closed maintenance camp for the pipeline on your left. (0.7)

7.1 Cross small creek. Triassic red beds and Jurassic Entrada Sandstone in cut bank. (0.9)

8.0 Top of hill. Route is on upper part of the Morrison Formation; the Purgatoire Formation is not readily recognized in this vicinity, but Dakota sandstone caps the ridge on your left. (1.3)

9.3 Ridge road to right. At 7:30 the creek drains eastward through a V-notch in the Dakota sandstone, which dips east. (1.5)

10.8 Road on Morrison Formation. At 1:00 Carrizozo Creek drains eastward through a V-notch in the east-dipping Dakota sandstone. (0.4)

11.2 Slab crossing of Carrizozo Creek; Guy post office (open 1910–1945) is on the left. (0.8)

12.0 Top of hill. Road is probably on Purgatoire Formation. The broad valley 3 miles ahead follows Corrumpa Creek, in the headwaters of the North Canadian River. Sierra Grande is to the right in the distance; Rabbit Ear Mountain at 11:00. (0.5)

12.5 MP 35. (0.7)

13.2 Road turns left, across the east-dipping beds of the Dakota Group on the steeper part of the Guy monocline. Road to right leads west toward Des Moines. (0.2)

13.4 Top of hill. Road on gravel of the Ogallala Formation for the next two miles. At 2:00 glimpses of the Dakota sandstone in the valley of Corrumpa Creek on the east (lower) side of the Guy monocline. (0.7)

16.1 Pipeline crossing. Road is on the upland surface, developed on the Ogallala Formation. (1.2)

17.3 Dry lake at right. The hill at 10:00 consists of the Ogallala Formation with a caliche cap. (0.7)

18.0 Road turns right (south). Rabbit Ear Mountain is visible in the distance straight ahead. Rabbit Ear Mountain was a prominent marker for the Santa Fe Trail. It is one of many volcanoes capping the huge lava field that extends westward nearly 50 miles to Sierra Grande and 24 miles in a north-south direction. The vents come in pairs or triplets in an east-southeast alignment. Ages range from 2.2 to 2.3 million years old. Sierra Grande is slightly older at 2.5 to 2.6 million years old. (1.0)

19.0 Road turns left (east). (2.0)

21.0 Road turns right (south). (1.2)

22.2 Top of hill. Several of the more prominent volcanoes can be seen from here: Rabbit Ear Mountain (6,070 feet) at 11; Bible Top Butte straight ahead; Mt. Dora (also known as Cieneguilla del Burro Mountain, 6,295 feet) at 1; Mount Clayton (Round Mountain, 6,677 feet) at 1:30; Sierra Grande (8,720 feet) at 3; and Capulin Mountain (8,215 feet) at 3:30. (3.2)

25.4 There's a spectacular outcrop of castellate sandstone from the Dakota Group on the right. Castellate weathering is the result of differential cementation of the different rock layers. The more well-cemented layers are most resistant to erosion and are left standing in relief.

Straight ahead in the cut bank of North Canadian River, which we are about to cross, about 15 feet of black shale of the Purgatoire Formation underlie the Dakota Group. (0.2)

Castellate Dakota sandstone at mile 25.4

25.6 McLaughlin Bridge across the North Canadian River (Corrumpa Creek). Dakota sandstone at road level. (1.3)

26.9 Top of hill. From 1:00 to 3:00 there are east-dipping beds of the Graneros Shale and underlying Dakota Group, on the southern extension of the Guy monocline. (1.7)

28.6 Road intersection; continue straight. Grandview School (abandoned) on the right. For the next 4 miles, the route is on the Ogallala Formation, except for the valleys, which are cut into the upper part of the Dakota Group. (1.7)

30.3 Road crosses the Santa Fe Trail, which is indistinct here. (0.7)

31.0 Bridge over Alamos Creek. Thin bedded shaly sandstone of the upper part of the Dakota Group in the cut bank. (0.7)

31.7 Top of hill, view southeast at 10:30 into the elongate crater of Rabbit Ear Mountain. (1.3)

33.0 Road turns left. Road is on the upper part of the Dakota Group for the next 1.2 miles. At 11:00 are caliche-capped buttes of Ogallala Formation. (1.5)

34.5 Road curves right; road on Ogallala Formation for a short distance. (0.5)

35.0 The mesa straight ahead is capped with basalt, which is underlain by less than 20 feet of the Ogallala Formation, and in turn is underlain by the Dakota Group. Rabbit Ear Mountain is at 11:00. (0.4)

35.4 Pavement begins. (0.3)

35.7 Bridge across Seneca (Cieneguilla) Creek. Clayton Lake is a mile upstream. The field at 1:00 is irrigated from a storage tank fed by water seeping from the Dakota sandstone. At 3:00 the green grass marks a seep at the base of the Dakota sandstone, one of the good water-bearing units of Union County. On the hill ahead, the Ogallala is thin, and the top foot is red because of baking when the overlying basalt lava flow covered it. Ahead, the road climbs Rabbit Ear Mesa, which is capped by several long, narrow tongues of basalt that issued from Mt. Dora or some other volcano to the west. These tongues are partly buried in places by later sheets of basalt from Rabbit Ear Mountain, Mt. Dora, and other nearby volcanoes. (1.3)

37.0 Junction with Clayton Lake road (NM-455). NM-370 continues straight ahead to Clayton. A short detour here to Clayton Lake State Park provides a look at some of

Sandstones of the Dakota Group were deposited as seas advanced from the north/northwest, in response to world-wide changes in sea level. This was the first advance of the Western Interior seaway, in the late Cretaceous.

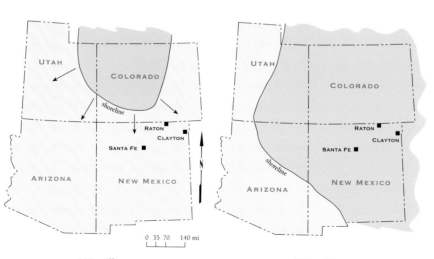

110 million years ago   100 million years ago

CLAYTON LAKE STATE PARK

The earth-fill dam for Clayton Lake was constructed in 1955 for the New Mexico Game and Fish Department. Although Seneca Creek has a modest base flow, the lake is primarily fed by flood water from rainstorms. The reservoir has a capacity of about 4,000

acre-feet, and the dam is about 75 feet high. During construction hundreds of dinosaur footprints were exposed in the spillway of the dam. Today they can be seen by walking to the far side of the dam. Excellent displays describe the various types of dinosaurs that made the footprints, and there are walkways over the footprints for closer viewing.

Several hundred footprints of four different species of dinosaurs are exposed in the spillway on the dam. Most of the tracks were made by large herbivorous ornithopod dinosaurs, such as *Iguanodon*. The heaviest of these, a three-toed dinosaur with a large heel pad, much like those illus-

trated here, left an impression of the entire foot. The largest of these tracks is 20 inches long and 17 inches wide. One trackway shows an ornithopod that was dragging its tail. The distorted footprints show that it was crossing unstable mud and probably using its tail for balance.

A smaller number of tracks are of carnivorous theropod dinosaurs, who walked on their toes with little or no heel depression. The largest footprint has a length and width of 16 inches. Some of the tracks line up to make trackways, which can provide insights into the size, weight, rate of movement, and whether the creature walked on its toes or its whole foot.

The tracks are found in sandstones from the Cretaceous Dakota Group (mostly in the Pajarito Formation). These sandstones form the walls of the valley

here. Exposed over a thickness of about three feet are two sandstone units separated by a zone of silt and clay-rich layers. It is in this silty zone that the dinosaur footprints are preserved. These layers contain ripple marks, cross bedding, and mud cracks (at left), features that are associated with river floodplains. The sand units mark the shorelines of the ocean at that time. Rivers from the northwest fed sediment into this region and drove the shoreline southeast. The silty layers mark the coastal plain and the overlying sandstone marks the retreat of the shoreline to the northwest.

the most spectacular (and accessible) dinosaur trackways in North America. (1.0)

38.0 Curve left. Ascend hill onto flows from Rabbit Ear Mountain. (1.0)

39.0 Road turns right. The plate on the southwest side of Rabbit Ear Mountain is probably all that remains of the outside surface of the volcano. The rest is evidently the coating on the inside of the crater. (1.8)

40.8 Descend hill onto an older basalt flow that may have come from Mt. Dora or a vent farther west. (2.1)

42.9 Road turns left. Apache Canyon ahead. (0.4)

43.3 Descend hill from basalt cap onto the Ogallala Formation, which is exposed in pit

on left. Up ahead, when the road curves to the left, the contact between the Ogallala Formation and the underlying Graneros Shale is marked by seeps and green grass. The walls of Apache Canyon are covered by landslides. (2.2)

45.5 Ascend hill. The top 5 feet of the Ogallala Formation was turned red (baked) by the heat of the overlying basalt flow. (0.5)

46.0 Top of Clayton Mesa. (1.4)

47.4 Stop at intersection of NM-370 with US-64/87. End of Trip 3. Downtown Clayton to the left.

Low aerial view of Clayton Lake from the southeast. Seneca Creek extends into the distance, at the north edge of an old lava flow.

Clayton to Raton via US–64/87

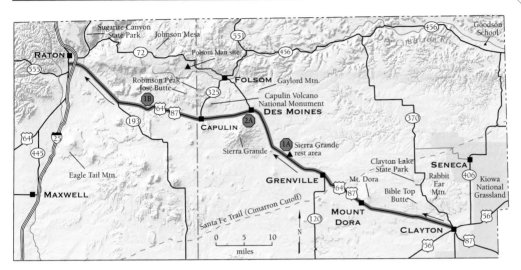

For the first 66 miles along US-64/87 we travel over gently rolling plains, broken only by the numerous extinct volcanoes that dot the landscape in every direction. Near Des Moines the road skirts the base of the huge Sierra Grande volcano. In this area we again see the three major subdivisions of basaltic lava flows that cover much of northeastern New Mexico: the Raton, Clayton, and Capulin Basalts. Although the flows are not as well exposed as they are east of Johnson Mesa along the route of Trip 1, there is perhaps a greater opportunity to understand more fully the complexities of the many flows that make up these three great rock units. In the last 25 miles of this trip we cross the highly dissected country of the Canadian River drainage system. Here are seen the Pierre Shale and Trinidad Sandstone of Cretaceous age and remnants of earlier

higher levels of the Canadian River and its tributaries that are now preserved as terraces. Altitudes along the route vary from a low of 4,900 feet at Clayton to between 6,500 and 7,000 feet from Des Moines to Raton. For greater flexibility the log is broken into two parts, as follows:

> Trip 4A: Clayton to the village of Capulin, 54 miles
>
> Trip 4B: Village of Capulin to Raton, 28 miles

From the village of Des Moines a very interesting and scenic loop drive of 22.6 miles to Folsom and Capulin Volcano National Monument (Trip 2) gives a closer look at the most recent sequence of eruptions known as the Capulin-age flows.

Unlike the remote northern route

from Raton to Clayton along the Dry Cimarron (Trip 1), this direct route from Clayton to Raton on US-64/87 is heavily traveled and can be dangerous. There are passing lanes in several places, but travelers are well advised to use extra caution on this stretch of road. Pull off only where pullouts have been provided

THE CITY OF CLAYTON

Clayton was founded in 1888 as a cattle shipping center for the railroad. From the 1880s through the 1950s cattle were shipped from Clayton to Kansas City, Chicago, Denver, and Fort Worth. Cattle buyers contracted directly with the ranches,

whose responsibility it was to get the livestock to the shipping pens, where they were weighed and loaded on the trains.

In 1889 a severe blizzard cut Clayton off from the outside world for several weeks; train service from the north was stopped for 13 days. The snow averaged 7 feet with drifts as high as 25 feet. Frozen cattle, horses, sheep, and cowboys were found when the snow melted. Cattle shipments from Clayton were mostly suspended for the winter, which was a severe blow to a railroad town. It took a year for Clayton to recover.

In the early 1890s Clayton prospered as a place for health seekers—well-bred, well-educated residents who endured hardships to regain their health in Clayton's climate. The Eklund Hotel, built in 1892, and the Union County Court House, built in 1909, are examples of the early Clayton architectural style. A story is told of Judge Mills, who was attending a formal party when he was called to the court house to receive a verdict. He arrived wearing evening clothes, heard the verdict, and adjourned the court. The next day a stranger asked if it was customary for the judge to preside in full dress; he was told that no man in Clayton would think of going out in the evening in anything but a full dress suit.

Clayton was known as a rough and ready railroad town until 1901. Pat Garrett was a well known rancher and sheriff in the area. Despite his reputation as a killer, he in fact killed only three men: Billy the Kid and his companions Tom O'Foliard and Bowdry, and those killings were in self defense.

Prosperity faded after World War I, and the Dust Bowl caused thousands of farmers

KIOWA NATIONAL GRASSLANDS

For those with extra time, Kiowa National Grasslands, near Mills, on NM-39, 16 miles south of Abbott (which is 62 miles west of Clayton on US-56) has a three mile segment along the Santa Fe Trail that is open for walking. For a shorter detour, go north on NM-370 for 10 miles to Clayton Lake State Park to see a spectacular display of dinosaur footprints.

to go bankrupt. Those who stayed switched from crops to cattle. Finally the Depression hit, but Clayton survived, partly because of a very successful WPA (Works Progress Administration) building project.

In 1958 the Five States Livestock Auction began business, and today thousands of cattle are brought from the surrounding ranches for sale in Clayton. With an estimated 100,000 cattle on surrounding ranches, cattle here still outnumber people 150/1. The auction is a weekly Wednesday social event where people from the five states of New Mexico, Colorado, Kansas, Oklahoma, and Texas gather to watch auction action and eat at the on-site cafe.

Today it is estimated that 85 percent of the local economy is dependent directly or indirectly on cattle, and Clayton considers itself a "cow town."

The Eklund Hotel in downtown Clayton, built in 1892, reopened in 2004 and now offers both dining and lodging.

BLACK JACK KETCHUM

Thomas E. "Black Jack" Ketchum was another notable character who added a macabre bit of lore to Clayton history. He and his gang were notorious train robbers. On the night of August 16, 1899, he attempted a daring robbery that he thought would become the crowning achievement of his wild career. At Twin Mountain Curve outside of Folsom he boarded the engine, captured the front-end crew, and ordered the rear express car cut away. Since it was on a curve, they could not pull the coupling pin, and during the delay the conductor shot Ketchum in the arm. He escaped but was caught the following day and treated at the Folsom Hotel. While awaiting trial in Clayton, his arm was amputated. Though there was not enough evidence to convict him of murder, train robbery carried a death penalty at that time in New Mexico, and Black Jack Ketchum was sentenced to hang. Because of his reputation and the fear that gang members would try to rescue him, a stockade was built around the gallows. Witnesses said he arrived at the gallows dressed in a white shirt, white bow tie, and black suit, with carefully polished shoes. Others remarked that he moved his head from side to side to help get the noose properly adjusted. When the nervous hangman fumbled it, Black Jack called out: "Hurry it up; I'm due in hell for dinner." The problem was that the noose was not adjusted correctly for his large stature; as the trap was sprung, he was decapitated—a bizarre end to a wild career. He was buried in an unmarked grave.

SCENIC TRIP FOUR-A (54 MILES)
Clayton to Capulin

0.0 Start at the traffic light in Clayton at the junction of NM-87 and NM-64. Travel on US 64/87 toward Raton. (0.4)

0.4 Junction with NM-370 to Clayton Lake, Guy, and the Dry Cimarron valley on right. Road bends left over Colorado and Southern Railway overpass. Rabbit Ear Mountain is the largest peak at 11:30. It is named for an Indian chief and was an important landmark even before the Santa Fe Trail existed. (0.3)

View from the north of Rabbit Ear Mountain, ten miles northwest of the town of Clayton. This Clayton-age volcano erupted 2.2-2.3 million years ago.

0.7 Straight ahead on the skyline is Mt. Dora (Cieneguilla del Burro Mountain), a huge extinct shield volcano, about 2.7 million years old. To the right and far behind it is Sierra Grande, the largest volcano in this region. It is 40 miles from here. Between 1:00 and 3:00 are four prominent volcanoes along the northern skyline. These large vents furnished the lava that caps the mesa on which they rest. Most of the lower hills along the skyline are small volcanoes. (0.1)

0.8 Road drops off the edge of the basalt-capped mesa on which Clayton is situated. Broad depression ahead (1.2 miles across) is rimmed by Clayton Basalt, except for the south margin, and is floored by Ogallala sand and gravel. The south rim is part of the ancient uplands into which the valley was cut. Later the Clayton basalt flowed down this valley. The Ogallala Formation extends east and south for several hundred miles and underlies the High Plains that extend north from Texas to Nebraska. The porous sands of the Ogallala make excellent reservoirs for water and because of this, ranching and some irrigation is possible on the plains. (1.3)

2.1 The road climbs back onto Clayton basalt. Basalt boulders can be seen on both sides of the road. The basalt that filled the valley is more resistant to erosion than are the surrounding softer rocks of the (older) Ogallala Formation. These softer rocks have been washed away, leaving what had been a stream valley now forming the high mesas between the modern stream valleys. (0.6)

2.7 The historic marker on the south side of the road calls attention to Rabbit Ear Mountain. These two striking mounds became important landmarks for travelers even before the Santa Fe Trail. Caravans on the Santa Fe Trail passed on both sides of the mountain, 860 miles out from Independence, Kansas, their starting point, and 230 miles from the end of the trail in Santa Fe. (0.4)

3.1 Once again we drop off the edge of the Clayton Basalt onto sands and gravels of the Ogallala Formation. (0.6)

3.7 Back up onto the Clayton Basalt cap. The tree and brush-covered rim, visible many miles to the south, is Dakota sandstone. (0.5)

4.2 Excellent view north to Apache Canyon, showing the basalt rim on both sides and the line of volcanoes and their lava flows on top of the mesa beyond. Bible Top Butte is the tilted flat-topped mountain at 1:30. Rabbit Ear Mountain is at 3:00. (1.8)

6.0 At 10:00, about 5 miles distant, is edge of Clayton Basalt tongue (black rim) that caps the mesa that, 6 miles to the west, joins the one on which we are driving. The mesa on the skyline from 8:00 to 10:00 is

capped with Dakota sandstone. (1.5)

7.5 MP 423. On the skyline at 3:00 is Bible Top Butte. The peak is flat-topped and has a crease parallel to the highway so that the basalt cap resembles an open book, hence the name. (0.6)

8.1 Road to Royce enters from right. At 1:00 the enormous size of Mt. Dora (sometimes known as Cieneguilla del Burro Mountain) can now be seen. In shape and probable habit when it erupted, it resembles the broad shield volcano type of the Hawaiian Islands. Nearly all of the material from the volcano was a very fluid lava that flowed rapidly away from the peak (vent),

STEPHEN W. DORSEY

Stephen W. Dorsey, Arkansas senator from 1873-79, eventually settled in New Mexico and lent his name to a number of fantastic endeavors, not the least of which was the home he built on the High Plains. Dorsey, with his lawyer Bob Ingersoll, started the Triangle Dot Ranch in Colfax and Union Counties. Such large herds were being driven from Texas to Springer, New Mexico and Granada, Colorado that a railroad was proposed through the northeast part of New Mexico. In the late 1880s Dorsey's ranch

foreman, John C. Hill, suggested they form a company, secure land on the proposed railroad right of way, and establish a trading post. They chose a site near Apache Springs, an important water source. Hill persuaded the construction manager for the Denver & Fort Worth Railroad Company to make the new town a stopping

point on the Colorado & Southern, a part of the Denver & Fort Worth system. The post office had been named Perico, and three days after the train arrived, on March 23, 1888, the name was changed to Clayton in honor of Senator Dorsey's son. Mt. Dora, an important landmark on the Santa Fe Trail, was named for his sister-in-law. Mt. Marguerite and other hills were named for various members of his family. The Dorsey Mansion still stands today, about 30 miles east of Springer.

The Dorsey Mansion.

forming the broad low volcano. (1.5)

9.6 Windmill on south side of road. This windmill is typical of hundreds in northeastern New Mexico that must penetrate the hard basalt cap before entering porous sands, which both the driller and the land owner hope will be full of good water. (2.4)

12.0 At 1:00 the head of Apache Canyon can be seen at the foot of Mt. Dora. At that point, the basalt mesa forming the north rim of Apache Canyon (and underlying Rabbit Ear Mountain at 5:00) joins the Clayton Basalt mesa upon which we are still driving. (4.0)

16.0 Mt. Dora (also known as Cieneguilla del Burro Mountain) at 3:00. At 12:30 is Sierra Clayton, another extinct volcano. In this region nearly any peak rising above the level of the plains and mesas is an extinct volcano. (1.6)

17.6 Town of Mt. Dora, formerly a stock-shipping station for the Colorado and Southern Railway. Sierra Grande is straight ahead on the horizon. (1.1)

18.7 Junction on left with NM-426 to Sofia. (1.3)

20.0 At 3:00 the low hill on the skyline is a small volcano along a line of volcanoes that includes Mt. Dora. At 10:30 is Sierra Clayton, a cinder cone. Steeply dipping layers of volcanic cinders can be seen on the flanks of the cone. The crater has been breached by streams. (3.2)

23.2 Picnic table at pullout on right. The first wagons on the Santa Fe Trail crossed here in 1822. No ruts are visible at this point. Ruts from the Santa Fe Trail can best be seen north of Clayton near Moses. (2.0)

25.2 Roadcut on left exposes the Clayton Basalt cap. This is the same lava flow we have been on since leaving Clayton. (1.1)

26.3 Grenville, altitude 5,990 feet. Former stock shipping station along Colorado and Southern Railway. Junction with NM-120 to Pasamonte. (1.2)

27.5 MP 403. Straight ahead (west) is Sierra Grande (8,729 feet), the largest volcano in this region, with Little Grande at the base (right down the highway). Straight behind us is Mt. Dora, the second largest volcano in the region. The unnamed large broad dome south of Sierra Grande (about 11:00) rates among the top five volcanoes in size in this region and appears to be the source of the lava on which we are driving.

Sierra Clayton is at 8:00. At 9:00 a few peaks of the fourteen aligned volcanoes of the Don Carlos Hills are on the distant skyline. At 4:00 is an Ogallala-capped mesa that was never covered by lava flows. The edges of a Clayton Basalt-capped mesa can be seen at 3:00. On the far horizon (10 miles away) is another basalt-capped mesa (called the Gaps Flow—one gap can be seen at about 3:00), which appears to be another tongue of the Clayton Basalt. (2.5)

30.0 The cuts along the railroad expose the top of the Clayton Basalt. (0.8)

30.8 Abandoned sand and gravel pits on south side of highway. (0.2)

31.0 Bridge. (0.5)

31.5 MP 399. (1.8)

33.3 At 10:00 on the far distant skyline are Palo Blanco Mountain (left) and 8,820-foot Laughlin Peak right behind Mt. Marcy (Malpie Mountain) on near skyline. The unnamed large broad volcano at 9:00 is composed of basalt identical with that on which we have been driving from Clayton. It probably supplied much of the lava that formed this wide basalt-covered flat. Other volcanoes also supplied this same type of lava, as for example, the unnamed volcano at 11:00. (3.2)

36.5 Little Grande is on the left (south) side of the road. Layers visible are eroded edges of lava flows interbedded with volcanic cinders. The small, steep-sided volcanoes, like this one, have a large proportion of cinders in contrast to the broad shield volcanoes, like Sierra Grande (ahead), which are mostly formed of fluid lava with only a minor amount of cinders. Complex cross-layering was formed because the vent changed its shape and direction of eruption during the formation of the volcano.

To the north, the plains are mostly covered by sands of the Ogallala Formation. On the remote skyline, at 3:00 the Seven-L Buttes, part of the Mesa de Maya in southern Colorado, can be seen on a clear day. In the middle distance at 4:00 is the north rim of the great Clayton Basalt sheet on which we have been riding. (1.3)

37.8 At right in gully are outcrops of basalt that exhibit crudely developed columnar jointing, caused by contraction during cooling of the basalt. At 2:00 the south edge of a basalt flow that extends east for 14 miles (Van Cleve Flow), similar in composition to that in the gully we just passed through (but slightly different from the Clayton Basalt whose northwest rim can be seen at 3:00). At 9:00 is a basaltic volcano that may have supplied lava to form the Van Cleve Flow. (0.4)

Cross-layering of cinders on Little Grande, at mile 36.5.

38.2 STOP 1 – Pull into rest area on the right and park. Sierra Grande is by far the largest and most imposing volcano in this region. It rises nearly 2,100 feet above the plains, placing its summit at 8,720 feet above sea level. It is 8 miles in diameter and has a composition that is unique to this region. It is a two-pyroxene andesite or olivine-free basalt, depending on terminology. Volcanic breccias are present around the crest, but no true crater remains from its eruption about 2.5 million years ago. Interestingly, there are no lava flows of this composition extending out from the base of this monster volcano. Instead, all the flows surrounding Sierra Grande are related to the extensive Clayton-age flow that we have

East flank of Sierra Grande.

beautiful (but worthless) tiny blue crystals of the rare mineral haüynite, one of the sodalite-lazurite group of minerals. (0.9)

41.5 A clear view of Gaylord Mountain can be had at 1:00. Behind it and to the left is a tree-covered mesa capped by Raton Basalt, the southeast end of the basalt rim that rises slowly westward until at Raton it is more than 1,000 feet above the city. On the mesa straight ahead is a Clayton-age volcano, Emery Peak (7,350 feet), an important key in the volcanic history in this region because lava from it blocked the Dry Cimarron River (beyond it from us). Into the lake that formed behind the lava dam poured basalt and stream deposits from many other volcanoes so that the sequence of 11 different volcanoes could be determined. This sequence is discussed at the beginning of Trip 1B.

We are still skirting the east base of Sierra Grande. The main bulk of the mountain is composed of pyroxene andesite, lighter-colored than the basalt we have seen because it contains more silica. (2.4)

been driving on from near the town of Clayton. At an altitude of 8,720 feet above sea level, Sierra Grande is high enough to intercept the summer rain clouds, so that the grass on it is wet and green even if the surrounding plains are dry and brown.

Exit at the far end of the rest area and continue west on NM-64/87 toward Raton. (0.7)

38.9 Ranch road enters from left. At 11:00 on near skyline is a small volcano that also may have supplied lava to form the Van Cleve Flow. (1.7)

40.6 Ranch road enters from left. Gaylord Mountain can be seen in the distance by sighting along the railroad track at 12:30. Some of the basalt from this vent contains

43.9 Des Moines village limit, altitude 6,622 feet. Des Moines is a trading and ranching center. Although the Colorado and Southern Railway erected a station here when it extended its lines through New Mexico in 1887-88, no town grew until 1907 when two town sites were surveyed and both were occupied. About 1916, the two towns grew together, and the name Des Moines was used for both. Drought and the depression caused the population to decline after its peak of about 800 people in 1920. In 1936 a rich carbon dioxide deposit was discovered and that started a dry ice industry that lasted for 30 years. Another blow came in 1940 when the Santa Fe, Raton and Eastern Railway was abandoned and the tracks were torn up. However, Des Moines is still an important shipping point on the Colorado & Southern Railroad.

At 2:30 on near skyline is Dunchee Hill, the eroded remnant of another volcano. (1.1)

45.0 Junction with NM-325 to Folsom. Trip 2 covers the route from here to Folsom and on to Capulin Volcano National Monument before rejoining US 64/87. Continue straight ahead toward Raton. (0.7)

Pass branch of the Goodnight-Loving Trail until 1875. In that year, he blazed the trail northward from Fort Sumner to near Tucumcari and Clayton. This was the last trail created by Goodnight marking the end of his operations in New Mexico.

We are near the crest of the Sierra Grande arch. The underlying bedrock here (of Cretaceous and older age rocks) forms a broad northerly-trending arch with the westward-sloping side extending to the center of the Raton Basin (just west of the town of Raton) before turning up again along the foot of the Sangre de Cristo Mountains. The eastward-sloping side of the arch continues

The Goodnight-Loving Trail, developed by Charles Goodnight (above) in the 1860s, was for years the main route for trailing cattle to Denver and the railroad east.

45.7 STOP 2 – Pull off at roadside tables on right. In the 1860s the Goodnight-Loving Trail provided a route for Texas cattlemen to drive their herds from Texas north to Colorado, where they could be shipped east. Charles Goodnight, the great Texas cattleman, used the Trinchera

with only gentle warps into Texas.

At 1:00 is Capulin Mountain (8,215 feet), a nearly perfectly preserved cinder cone. The road carved into its side goes up to the lower edge of the crater. From there, the visitor has a spectacular view to the Sangre de Cristo Mountains, and on the walk around the rim of the crater spectacular views in all directions.

Behind Capulin and at its right base is José Butte. To its right and slightly nearer on the mesa top is Robinson Peak; both are Clayton-age volcanoes. In front of Robinson Peak and low in the valley is the ruddy-colored Mud Hill, a Capulin-age volcano. All three of these poured volcanic material, lava, and cinders into the lake behind the Emery Peak lava dam. Only the top of Emery Peak is visible at 3:00.

At 1:30 on the distant skyline is tree-covered Red Mountain, a volcano similar in composition to Sierra Grande. It is on top of Johnson Mesa, which in turn is held up by the Raton Basalt, which forms the forested skyline from Red Mountain to 2:00. For details of this area see Trip 1A. (0.4)

46.1 Large depression on the right (meadow in dry years and lake in wet) was formed in much the same manner as were the oases in northeastern Africa. Wind removed the cap of uncemented sand (Dakota Group) down to a muddy layer that is always damp and thus adheres together. This dampness stopped the downcutting by the wind (deflation). Along the east rim are sand dunes (mostly covered by vegetation)

Capulin Mountain from US 64/87. A cinder vent formed the high cone; liquid lava poured from the crater in the low ridge on the left side of the cone. The end of one lava flow is visible in the foreground.

formed by the deposition of the sand blown out of the depression. The depressions of northern Africa are bottomed at the natural ground water level. This keeps the sand moist and sticking together. The big sand "seas" of the Sahara Desert are downwind from giant depressions.

Abandoned railroad grade from Des Moines to Raton parallels the road to right. It can be seen at many places near the highway. (1.2)

47.3 Ranch road enters from left. Small juniper trees cover much of the lower slopes of Sierra Grande. Higher on the slopes are ponderosa pine and spruce. (0.2)

47.5 Approximate crest of Sierra Grande arch. West from here the Cretaceous and older rocks slope westward, and east from here they slope eastward. Along the northern skyline are the forested rims of grass-covered mesas of Raton Basalt. Living snow fence on the right. (0.9)

48.4 Ranch road enters from the left. At 11:00 is the barren, round, humped shape of Horseshoe Mountain, a volcano of about the same age as Capulin Mountain. Behind it and to its left is Palo Blanco Mountain. To the right and behind Horseshoe is Laughlin Peak. (0.2)

48.6 Road crosses abandoned railroad grade. Gravel pit in the Ogallala Formation at 3:00. (0.8)

49.4 Ranch road enters from right. Straight ahead basalt from Capulin Mountain flowed southward as far as the highway. In doing so it buried a stream valley. Springs issue forth

from gravels in that early buried valley near the grove of trees at 2:30.

To the right and a mile beyond the springs is a mesa capped with the southeasternmost extension of the Raton Basalt; it overlies the orange-stained sands of the Ogallala Formation. Other extensions of the Raton Basalt can be seen ahead, capping the mesa between 11:00 and the highway and capping the south-sloping mesa (left) on the distant skyline straight ahead.

The road spiraling up Capulin Mountain gives the visitor to the monument excellent views of the surrounding countryside as well as the layering of cinders on the flanks of the cone. At 9:00 is another unnamed volcano. (1.1)

50.5 MP 380. (0.7)

51.2 Abandoned railroad grade in foreground on right. Beyond it across narrow valley is edge of Capulin Mountain basalt.

Extending diagonally to the right rear from the foot of the basalt straight ahead is a road now marked by old telephone lines that follow another route of the old Fort Union-Fort Dodge military wagon road of Santa Fe Trail days. This road went over Trinchera Pass north of Folsom into Colorado. (0.7)

51.9 Roadcut on right in tip of basalt flow from Capulin Mountain. Capulin Mountain basalt is unique for this region: it has large (nearly ¼-inch-long) plagioclase and small green olivine crystals. No other vent in this region has this combination of crystals.

Road now is between Capulin Mountain basalt on the right (north) and the southeasternmost outlier of Raton Basalt on the left (south).(0.7)

52.6 Historic Marker on right. (1.1)

53.7 Capulin village. Junction with NM-325 to Capulin Mountain and Folsom. End of Trip 4A. The Capulin Country Store at this intersection is a good choice for lunch and/or supplies (and there are limited opportunities for such between Clayton and Rayon).

Capulin Mountain, a classic cinder cone. Dark gray lava in the foreground poured out of fractures near the base of the cone.

SCENIC TRIP FOUR-B (28 MILES)
Clayton to Capulin

0.0 Intersection of NM-325 and US 64/87. Reset tripmeter to 0.0 and proceed west toward Raton. (0.5)

0.5 Cross abandoned railroad grade. On skyline on the right is Robinson Peak. José Butte at 2:30 is partially hidden by the ruddy columns of Raton Basalt that hold up the mesa. In the middle ground are basalt flows from Capulin Mountain. The low basin that the road crosses for the next mile is Capulin Basin. It drained eastward before the eruption of Capulin, and now no surface water escapes from this closed depression. But, water seeps underground and appears at the springs described at mile 50.2. Horseshoe Mountain at 9:30. Rain running down its slopes caused the grooves. Clayton-age basalt caps the mesa straight ahead. (0.2)

0.7 MP 376. Colfax County line. (0.3)

2.0 This is a good place to see the elevation differences of the three major groups of basalt in this region and thus determine the relative ages of the basalt flows. The ruddy, tree-covered cliffs at 2:00 and 3:00 are held up by the oldest group, named Raton Basalt. José Butte, a Clayton-age volcano at 2:30 on skyline, erupted through the Raton Basalt cap; lava then flowed southward over the Raton Basalt edge (at 2:15) to fill the valley that then existed. Removal of the surrounding softer rocks by erosion has left the valley standing as a low mesa between 1:00 and 2:00 (behind the ranch buildings at 1:30). The youngest volcanoes, the Capulin Basalt, flowed into the present valley bottoms, and during the past few tens of thousand years they have been partially buried here by material blown or washed into the low areas. (1.0)

3.0 Road crosses abandoned railroad grade. (0.6)

3.6 José Butte at 3:00. To the south are several large volcanoes, which, because of

their light color and composition, are grouped with the Red Mountain Dacites. At 8:30 is Palo Blanco Mountain; at 9:00 on the distant skyline are the pair known as Timber Buttes (mesa cap to left and in front of them is the Raton Basalt-capped Kiowa Mesa). At 10:00 is Laughlin Peak.

Red Mountain is on the top of Johnson Mesa and is hidden from view to the north by the nearer mesas and volcanoes. From 10:00 to 11:00 on the skyline is the south-sloping narrow Raton Basalt-capped Larga Mesa. At 11:30 extending south is a Clayton Basalt flow. At 12:30 on the distant skyline is Raton Basalt-capped Dry Mesa. (1.2)

4.8 Road climbs onto basalt flow of Capulin age. This is the oldest Capulin flow we know about, with an age of 1.44 million years (a somewhat anomalously old flow for Capulin-age basalts). (2.2)

7.0 Still on basalt from the Capulin-age vents that are about 3 miles north but are hidden behind the grassy ridge at 2:30. Lava came around both sides of the ridge and moved toward us. The grassy meadow with the windmill in the middle ground was not covered by the lava. At 3:00 the grassy hill is an older Clayton-age volcano.

On the distant skyline to the north is Raton Basalt-capped Johnson Mesa. On it at 2:30 is Bellisle Mountain (8,520 feet), from which a lava flow went east into the Emery Peak lava dam. At 3:30 is Red Mountain, for which the Red Mountain Dacite is named. The round knob on the skyline is an outlying remnant of Raton Basalt no longer connected to Johnson Mesa.

Dry Mesa at 1:00 shows a double set of

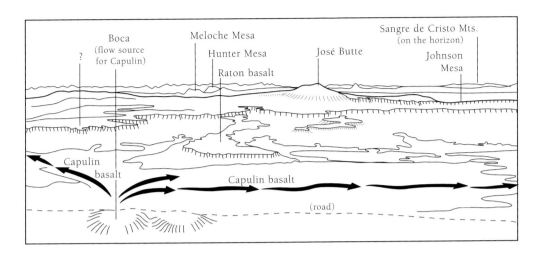

Boca
(flow source
for Capulin)
?
Meloche Mesa
Hunter Mesa
Raton basalt
José Butte
Sangre de Cristo Mts.
(on the horizon)
Johnson
Mesa
Capulin
basalt
Capulin basalt
(road)

View west from the parking area on the rim of Capulin Mountain. The snow-capped Sangre de Cristo Mountains are visible on the distant skyline.

columnar joints; here each set represents one lava flow. Some basalt flows form two sets of joints, a short, stubby set below and tall, narrow ones on top. The upper ones are longer and narrower as a result of the more rapid cooling possible because of exposure to wind and rain. (1.8)

8.8 Grade off west edge of the Capulin-age basalt. At right is a gully undercutting columnar-jointed basalt. At left is abandoned railroad grade. (1.7)

10.5 North end of Raton Basalt-capped Larga Mesa at 9:00. Unnamed Clayton-age volcano at 10:00. In gap at 9:30 is Laughlin Peak. (0.3)

10.8 In roadcut on right are brown-weathering pieces of limy and sandy mud rocks in which a few extinct oysters and marine worm burrows can be found. These fossils show that this area was under the sea during Late Cretaceous time. (0.2)

11.0 The ridge on the left is Clayton Basalt. On the right, the ridge is formed of the limy and sandy layers in the Upper

Cretaceous black shales. The right skyline is Dry Mesa, held up by columnar-jointed Raton Basalt. Straight ahead are the distant peaks of the Sangre de Cristo Mountains. In front of them in the middle distance are the mesa rims of the Trinidad Sandstone, part of the Cretaceous coal-producing sequence that extends from Cimarron, New Mexico northward to Pueblo, Colorado. (1.1)

12.1 Roadcut on right (north) and stream valley on left expose sandy and limy beds of Upper Cretaceous Pierre Shale with fragments of oysters and clams. (0.3)

12.4 STOP 1 - Pullout on right. Official Scenic Historic Marker marks the Rocky Mountains, which are visible on the distant horizon to the west. The Sangre de Cristo range of the Southern Rocky Mountains visible here includes the Spanish Peaks in Colorado, and the Culebra and Cimarron Ranges in New Mexico. The highest peaks visible attain altitudes of more than 13,000 feet above sea level.

Aerial view of the west end of Johnson Mesa, looking east/northeast.

Clear view ahead toward Cunningham Butte and Black Mesa in middle distance straight ahead. Small knobs at 12:30 are Clayton Basalt. High mesas at 1 are Meloche Mesa (composed of Red Mountain Dacite) and East Meloche Mesa. At 3:00 on the skyline is Buckhorn Mesa, capped by Clayton-aged basalt. Dry Mesa (Raton Basalt) is visible at at 4:00. (0.6)

13.0 On the skyline at 10:00 is Green Mountain, composed of Red Mountain Dacite. At 11:00 is an outlying remnant of Clayton-age basalt. (1.8)

14.8 Entrance to TO Ranch headquarters on right. Meloche Mesa at 2:30, East Meloche Mesa at 3:00. At 9:00 is tree-covered Green Mountain. At 8:30 is a grass-covered Clayton-age volcano with basalt flows extending nearly to Round Mesa at 11:00. At 10:00 is Eagle Tail Mountain, a Clayton-age volcano. Another unnamed Clayton-age volcano is the flat-topped peak at 9:30.

We will be driving on flats cut across the Upper Cretaceous Pierre Shale for the remainder of the distance to Raton. In places the shale is covered by a thin veneer of gravel or soil. (0.8)

15.6 Junction with NM-193. (2.1)

17.7 Ranch roads enter from both sides. Hunter Mesa (skyline point at 2:30) like Meloche Mesa (3:00) is held up by Red Mountain Dacite. Johnson Mesa at 1:00 to 2:00 on the distant skyline is held up by Raton Basalt as is Bartlett Mesa north of Raton at 12:15.

Clayton Basalt-capped mesas at 9:30

MILLS CANYON

Fifty miles south of here in Harding County, the Canadian River has cut a 600-feet-deep canyon through the Mesozoic strata of the High Plains of northeastern New Mexico. Mills Canyon, as it is known, is on the Kiowa National Grasslands and includes a 12-mile stretch of the Canadian River. Access to Mills Canyon today is via a dirt road that heads west from highway 39 near the town of Mills, between Abbott and Roy, southeast of Springer. The turnoff for Mills Canyon is signed; turn west from highway 39 onto a dirt road and follow it for approximately 6 miles to the edge of the canyon. From there a steep dirt road (impassable in wet weather) descends to the bottom of the canyon and a small primitive campground at the edge of the Canadian River.

Heading west from Mills the road crosses the Carlile Shale, the Greenhorn Formation, and the Graneros Shale. Cretaceous sandstones of the Dakota Group are exposed at the canyon rim. The road then descends through the Upper and Middle Jurassic section to the brightly colored Chinle Group (Triassic), exposed at the river.

The Kiowa National Grassland is administered by the Cibola National Forest. These grasslands provided forage for grazing animals for many years. Native buffalo were replaced by livestock introduced first by Spanish settlers and later by immigrants from the East. Farmers later removed the native vegetation to make way for crops, which proved to be a serious mistake when the 1930s drought brought the Dust Bowl to northeastern New Mexico. Eventually the federal government purchased much of the land and began to reestablish the native grasslands. Today these grasslands furnish feed for cattle and wildlife and provide protection to important watersheds. The successful restoration of game and bird habitat has fostered the growth of resident bird and animal populations.

For more information, contact the Kiowa and Rita Blanca National Grasslands at 714 Main Street in Clayton (505-374-9652).

frame Cunningham Butte (behind them) composed of Red Mountain Dacite. (1.0)

18.7 At 10:00 is Black Mesa, capped with Clayton-age basalt. Straight ahead on distant skyline is one of the Spanish Peaks in Colorado. (0.7)

19.4 At 1:30 is the southwest point of Johnson Mesa. About half way down is a point held up by an orangish-white layer, the Trinidad Sandstone. This band of light-colored sand can be traced as patches sticking through the landslide cover until at 2:30 it nearly meets the Raton Basalt cap.

Coal is found in the Trinidad Sandstone and associated formations. The region that has been extensively mined is west and north of Raton, although smaller workings are present in the flanks of Johnson Mesa.

The light-colored bands of the Trinidad Sandstone can be seen on the bluffs beyond Raton where the belt can be traced by eye from 10:30 to 3. (0.8)

20.2 At this point the road drops off an earlier broad flat stream valley down to the level cut by the modern Canadian River. Remnants of another slightly younger valley bottom can be seen ahead where the road is cut through the end of the terrace. Pierre Shale in roadcut under the stream gravel veneer. (0.3)

20.5 Terrace on the left is a remnant of the old valley we just left. (0.2)

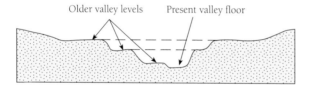

Older valley levels   Present valley floor

20.7 MP 356. Black Mesa on the skyline to the left. (0.2)

20.9 On the right the eroded edge of an older valley now above the present valley is visible. (0.9)

21.8 Roadcut in "paper shale" of Pierre Shale. Upper surface is gravel floor of abandoned valley. In the distance between 9:00 and 10:00 the difference in altitude between several remnants of the older stream valleys

can be seen. The present stream valley (with trees and bridge) has two distinct benches (terraces) of older valleys beyond it. (0.9)

22.7 Road drops off edge of older valley into modern valley of Chicorica Creek. (0.3)

23.0 On the right we can see the older valley rimming the present valley. (0.8)

23.8 Bridge over Chicorica Creek. (0.3)

24.1 Ranch road enters from right. At 10:00 is a gravel pit in older valley fill. (0.2)

24.3 Begin climb onto next older terrace. Stream gravel in roadcuts. (0.2)

24.5 Road continues up onto a still older terrace. (1.2)

25.7 On the skyline to the right is Barilla Mesa, capped by Raton Basalt. (0.6)

26.3 Official Scenic Historic Marker for the city of Raton. Once the Willow Springs freight stop on the Santa Fe Trail, the town of Raton developed from A.T. & S.F. repair shops established when the railroad crossed Raton Pass in 1879. Valuable coal deposits attracted early settlers. Nearby Clifton House was a stagecoach stop until the Santa Fe Trail was abandoned after 1879. (0.7)

27.0 Overpass over I-25. (0.5)

27.5 Raton. I-25 interchange. End of Trip 4B.

SUGGESTED READING

HISTORY

The Santa Fe Trail: Its History, Legends, and Lore by David Dary. Alfred A. Knopf, 2001.

The Smithsonian Guide to Historic America: the Desert States by M. S. Durham. Stewart, Tabori and Chang, 1990.

Girl on a Pony by Laverne Hanners. University of Oklahoma Press, 1994.

The Lords of the Valley by Laverne Hanners. University of Oklahoma Press, 1996.

Roadside History of New Mexico by F. L. and R. B. Fugate. Mountain Press Publishing Company, 1989.

The WPA Guide to 1930s New Mexico. University of Arizona Press, 1989. Compiled by the workers of the Writers Program of the Works Project Administration for the State of New Mexico, it was originally published in 1940 as New Mexico: A Guide to the Colorful State, this guide contains a wealth of information on the history and development of New Mexico. Road logs cover most of the major highways in New Mexico and include numerous stops at important geologic and historic sites near the route.

Search for the First Americans by David J. Meltzer. St. Remy Press and Smithsonian Institution, 1993.

GEOLOGY

A Short History of Planet Earth by J. D. MacDougall. John Wiley & Sons, 1998.

New Mexico Geologic Highway Map (1:1,000,000). New Mexico Geological Society, 2005. The fully revised edition of a longtime favorite includes New Mexico geology, cross sections, geologic columns, resource maps, and a satellite image of the state.

Dinosaur Tracks of Western North America by Martin Lockley, Adrian Hunt, and Paul Koroshetz. Columbia University Press, 1999.

Volcanoes of North America, Charles A. Wood and Jurgen Kienle, editors. Cambridge University Press, 1990. A comprehensive listing of all volcanoes and volcanic fields of North America, with brief descriptions of each, ages, photos, and information on how best to see them.

Geologic Studies of Union County, New Mexico by Brewster Baldwin and William Muehlberger. New Mexico Bureau of Geology and Mineral Resources, Bulletin 63, 1959. Although technical in its approach, this remains an important reference.

Northeastern New Mexico: Guide to the New Mexico Geological Society 38th Annual Field Conference, Spencer G. Lucas and Adrian P. Hunt, editors. New Mexico Geological Society, 1987. Although somewhat technical and nearly 20 years old, this guidebook is an important reference for those seeking more detailed information on this region of the country. Includes additional road logs.

GLOSSARY

agate a transparent or translucent variety of quartz which has a waxy luster and in which the different colors are in bands, clouds, or distinct groups.

alluvium a general term for all detrital material deposited by modern rivers, thus including the sediments laid down in river beds, floodplains, lakes, or fans.

andesite a volcanic rock composed principally of plagioclase feldspar.

angular unconformity the older strata dip at an angle different from the younger strata, the two angles of dip meeting at a surface of erosion cut on the older strata.

anticline a fold in which the beds dip away from a common axis.

arkose a coarse-grained, feldspar-rich sandstone composed of poorly sorted angular grains, whose source material is usually derived from the disintegration of granitic rocks.

artesian water ground water that is under sufficient pressure to rise above the level at which it is encountered in a well. The water may or may not rise above the surface of the ground.

ash fragments blown from a volcano about the size of beach sand or smaller.

augite a mineral belonging to the pyroxene group composed of a silicate of calcium, magnesium and iron.

basalt a dark-colored, dense to fine-grained igneous rock consisting of the minerals feldspar (generally the plagioclase feldspars bytownite or labradorite, which are silicates of calcium, sodium, and aluminum) olivine, and pyroxene (silicates containing iron and magnesium).

basin a large depressed area with strata dipping inward toward a common axis.

bombs volcanic fragments, from the size of an apple upward, blown from a volcano.

butte an isolated hill or mountain separated from a mesa by erosion, thus a small mesa.

calcite a mineral whose composition is $CaCO_3$ (see calcium carbonate).

calcium carbonate ($CaCO_3$) a solid, occurring in nature as the mineral calcite, and as the rock limestone.

caliche gravel, sand, silt, etc., cemented by calcium carbonate. Also may consist of almost pure calcium carbonate. Occurs at the surface or near the base of the upper soil layers.

carbon dioxide (CO_2) A heavy, colorless gas, when solid is known as dry ice.

cephalopod a marine invertebrate that in most fossil forms consists of a calcareous shell divided into numerous chambers. Living forms are the pearly nautilus, squid, and octopus.

chalcedony a transparent to translucent variety of quartz having a waxy luster. May be white, blue, brown, gray, or black.

cinders nut-sized fragments blown from a volcano during eruption.

clastic plug a sandstone mass that cuts across the bedding of a sedimentary formation. May refer to collapse features or features that have been intruded as mobile sand either from above or below.

clay a material with plastic properties made up of grains less than 1/256 mm.

crater a steep-walled depression on top of a volcanic cone above the pipe or vent that feeds the volcano.

cross bedding internal lamination of strata inclined to the bedding planes of sedimentary rocks.

dacite a volcanic rock consisting of the minerals feldspar (both plagioclase and orthoclase feldspars, which are silicates of sodium, calcium and aluminum), quartz, and dark minerals such as pyroxene.

dike a tabular body of igneous rock that cuts across another rock or rocks.

dip the angle between a horizontal line and the inclination of any planar feature, such as a sedimentary layer.

erosion lowering of ground surface through removal of material by streams or wind.

extrusive referring to those igneous rocks that cool relatively quickly at the earth's surface—i.e., volcanic rocks like basalt, andesite, etc.

fault a fracture in rocks along which one side has moved relative to the other side.

fissure vent an elongate crack in the earth's surface from which lava or pyroclastic material has erupted.

fold a bend in any planar structure.

formation a rock unit, established for convenience of mapping or description, consisting of one or more types of rocks deposited essentially without interruption and usually distinctive from rock units above and below.

gravel unconsolidated, water-transported rock or mineral fragments ranging in size from 2 mm up.

group a rock unit combining two or more formations.

gypsum a colorless, or white, gray, brown, red, black or yellow mineral made up of calcium, sulfur, oxygen, and water. Varieties are selenite, alabaster, satin spar and others. Used to make plaster of Paris and gypsum board insulation. Soft enough to scratch with a finger nail.

haüyne a mineral of the sodalite group consisting of a silicate of sodium, calcium and aluminum.

hematite an oxide of iron (Fe_2O_3). May be of red earthy color or metallic appearing. Principal ore of iron.

igneous a rock that has formed from molten material. Igneous rocks can crystallize at or near the surface (as in extrusive, volcanic rocks like basalt) or deep beneath the surface (as in intrusive rocks, like granite).

intrusive referring to igneous rocks that cool slowly at depth beneath the earth's surface—for example, granite.

landslide a mass of earth, rock, or mixture of the two, which becomes loosened and slides or falls down a slope.

lava fluid rock that issues from a volcano or fissure in earth's surface; also applied to this same material after it solidifies.

limestone a bedded sedimentary deposit consisting chiefly of calcite.

malpais Spanish for "bad lands," usually applied to the rough surfaced areas covered by basalt.

mesa a flat-topped surface bounded on all sides by a steep cliff.

monocline a fold in which the amount of dip of the beds changes from gentle to steep and back to gentle, usually with the beds inclined in a single direction.

mudstone a hardened sedimentary deposit made up of particles of clay and silt.

plunge pool a pit in the stream bottom occurring at the foot of a waterfall.

pressure ridge an elongate wrinkling of the crust of a lava flow, apparently caused by the viscous drag of lava moving beneath a solidified crust.

sand unconsolidated grains ranging in size from $1/16$ to 2 mm.

sandstone a hardened sedimentary deposit consisting of grains of minerals or rocks of sand size ($1/16$-2 mm). Most sandstones consist largely of quartz (SiO_2).

shale a finely laminated, hardened sediment composed of particles mostly of clay size ($<1/256$ mm).

silt unconsolidated grains ranging in size from $1/256$ to $1/16$ mm.

siltstone a hardened sedimentary deposit consisting of grains of silt size.

slickenside a polished fault surface that shows lineations or striations caused by friction due to fault movement. The striations often indicate the direction of movement along the fault.

slush pit a hole dug in the ground to store the water or mud used in drilling a well with a rotary drilling rig.

talus rock fragments piled up at the bottom of a steep slope or cliff.

terrace relatively flat benches on a hillside, generally remnants of former stream valleys.

tholeiite a silica-rich basalt, characterized by the presence of low-calcium pyroxenes.

type locality the specific location where a formation is typically displayed and from which it is named. The name coming from a local physiographic or cultural feature such as a town or rail siding, or a hill or creek.

volcano a vent in the earth's crust from which molten lava, pyroclastic material, volcanic gases, etc. issue.

A Word About Maps

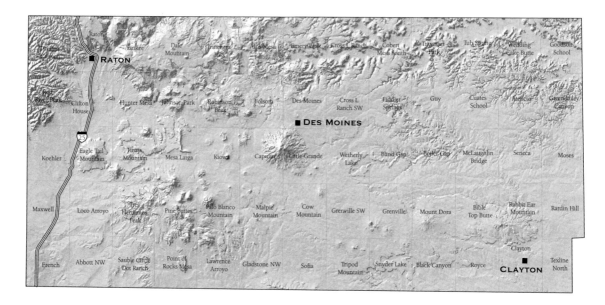

The index map above shows the distribution of 7 1/2-minute quadrangles across the scenic trip area. These maps and a wide variety of other maps and publications are available from the New Mexico Bureau of Geology and Mineral Resources in Socorro. The bureau carries a complete inventory of U. S. Geological Survey maps for the state of New Mexico. Visit our Publication Sales Office on the campus of New Mexico Tech in Socorro, phone us at (505) 835-5410, or visit our Web site at www.geoinfo.nmt.edu

A wide selection of map products are also available in Albuquerque at:

Holman's
6201 Jefferson NE
Albuquerque, NM 87109
(505) 343-0007

Recreational Equipment Incorporated (REI)
1550 Mercantile Avenue NE
Albuquerque, NM 87107
(505) 247-1191

INDEX

A

Adams, Gordon 57
agate 37, 48, 66, 88
Ancestral Rockies 12
Apache Canyon 70, 75, 76
Atchison, Topeka and Santa Fe Railroad 21
Atlantic and Pacific Railroad 21
Augite Vents 34, 35, 55

B

Baby Capulin 5, 6, 32, 34, 36, 39, 53, 58, 63
Baby Capulin Basalt 35, 36, 37, 38, 39, 55, 56, 58
Baldy Hill 40, 41
Baldy Hill Formation 21, 41
Barilla Mesa 24, 26, 27, 86
Bartlett Mesa 16, 17, 22, 84
Battleship Mountain. See Steamboat Butte
Bellisle basalt 7, 17, 30, 32
Bellisle Mountain 16, 28, 30, 34, 82
Bellisle Mountain Basalt 30, 32, 33
Bent's Fort 22
Bible Top Butte 67, 75
Big Hill 34, 36, 55
bison 1, 30, 31
Bison antiquus 30, 31
Black Mesa 27, 46, 84, 85, 86
bocas 61
bombs 4, 59, 63, 88
Bravo Dome field 54
buffalo. See bison
Burchard Ranch 57

C

caliche 33, 49, 67, 68, 88
Canadian River 17, 21, 50, 66, 67, 71, 85, 86
Capulin Hotel 57
Capulin Mountain 3, 5, 6, 7, 8, 9, 16, 17, 28, 30, 32, 33, 34, 53, 54, 55, 57, 58, 59, 60, 61, 62, 63, 64, 67, 79, 80, 81, 82
Capulin Volcano National Monument 19, 53, 59, 61-64, 71, 79, 92
Capulin, town of 7, 33, 53, 57, 60, 64, 81
Capulin-age basalts 53, 54, 59, 60, 82, 83
Carlisle Shale 20, 85
Carr Mountian 17
Carrizozo Creek 47, 66
castellate weathering 67
cephalopods 32
Chicorica Coal Company 26
Chicorica Creek 19, 25, 86
Chinle Group 7, 15, 37, 38, 39, 40, 44, 85
Cieneguilla del Burro Mountain 4, 52, 67, 74, 75, 76
Cieneguilla River 21, 47
Cimarron Cutoff 51, 52
Cimarron Range 84
cinder cones 3, 5, 6, 9, 17, 31, 32, 53, 58, 63, 76, 79, 81
cinders 3, 5, 9, 31, 55, 58, 59, 63, 76, 77, 80, 81, 88
clastic plugs 42, 43, 44, 46, 88
Clayton Basalt 7, 7, 17, 20, 28, 71, 74, 75, 76, 77, 82, 83, 84
Clayton Lake 13, 65, 68, 69, 70, 72, 74, 92
Clayton Mesa 4, 70
Clayton, city of 1, 6, 7, 9, 13, 15, 18, 56, 72-73
Clayton-age basalts 6, 30, 31, 34, 47, 48, 49, 52, 53, 54, 55, 60, 84
Clovis site 31, 95
Colorado 3, 9, 14, 16, 21, 22, 27, 29, 36, 37, 41, 47, 49, 53, 73, 77, 79, 81, 84, 85
Colorado and Southern Railway 32, 33, 53, 54, 55, 57, 74, 76, 78, 79
Colorado Interstate Gas Company 66

Colorado Museum of Natural History. See
    Denver Museum of Nature and Science
Corrumpa Creek 50, 51, 66, 67. See also
    North Canadian River
Cretaceous/Tertiary boundary 13, 21, 23, 25
Cross L Ranch House 39
crossbedded sandstone 38
Culebra Range 84
Cunningham Butte 84, 85

D

Dakota Group 7, 13, 15, 21, 35, 36, 37, 38,
    39, 40, 41, 42, 45, 46, 47, 48, 49, 50,
    51, 53, 55, 58, 65, 66, 67, 68, 69, 80,
    85, 95
Dale Mountain. See Bellisle Mountain
Denver Museum of Nature and Science 31
Des Moines 9, 53, 54, 62, 67, 71, 78, 79,
    80
Devoy, Madison 38
Devoys Peak 36, 38
dinosaur trackways 1, 13, 69
Dockum Group 39
Doherty Mercantile 56, 58
Don Carlos Hills 6, 62, 76
Dorsey Mansion 75
Dorsey, Stephen W. 75
Dry Cimarron Canyon 55, 56
Dry Cimarron River 6, 9, 1, 16, 17, 19, 20,
    21, 30, 31, 32, 34, 35, 36, 37, 38, 40,
    41, 42, 43, 47, 54, 56, 57, 65, 78
Dry Cimarron Valley 33, 48, 58, 74
Dry Mesa 82, 84
Dunchee Hill 54, 79
Dust Bowl 6, 72, 85

E

Eagle Tail Mountain 17, 84
East Big Hill 34, 36
East Emery Peak 34, 36, 37, 54
Eklund Hotel 72, 73

Emery Gap 36, 37
Emery Peak 15, 33, 34, 35, 36, 54, 55, 78
Emery Peak Basalt 34, 35, 36, 37, 55
Emery, Madison 37
Ensign Ranch House 26
Entrada Sandstone 13, 21, 37, 38, 39, 40,
    41, 42, 43, 44, 45, 46, 48, 65, 66
Eocene Epoch 14
Evans, Max 1
extinctions 1, 13

F

Fisher's Peak Mesa 15, 17
Folsom 1, 16, 19, 31, 33, 36, 53, 56-57
Folsom Falls Fishing Area 35-36
Folsom Hotel 56, 58, 73
Folsom Man 1, 19, 30. See Denver
    Museum of Nature and Science
Folsom point 30, 31
Folsom Vents 31, 34
Fort Dodge 33, 55, 81
Fort Hays Limestone 13, 20, 32
Fort Union 22, 33, 36, 51, 55, 81
Fort Union National Monument 33

G

Gaylord Mountain 54, 78
Girl on a Pony 46
Gleason Canyon 40
Goat Hill 13, 21, 22, 23
Goodnight, Charles 56, 79
Goodnight-Loving Trail 1, 35, 36, 55, 56,
    79
Goodson School 45, 46
Grandview School 67
Graneros Shale 48, 49, 51, 67, 70, 85
Green Mountain 84
Greenhorn Formation 13, 20, 85
Grey, Zane 1
Guy monocline 41, 66, 67

H

Hanners, LaVerne 5, 46
haüyne 7, 17, 89
Hereford Park 30
High Plains aquifer 14
Horse Mesa 15, 25, 26, 27
Horseshoe Mountain 5, 28, 60, 64, 80, 82
Hunter Mesa 24, 84

I

Iguanodon 69
inversion of topography 4, 15
iridium 21, 23
isotopic ages 15

J

Jemez Lineament 9
Johnson Mesa 10, 4, 6, 7, 15, 16, 17, 19,
    20, 22, 24, 27, 28, 29, 30, 34, 35, 55,
    71, 80, 82, 83, 84, 85, 86
José Butte 5, 9, 28, 30, 34, 54, 57, 59, 60,
    63, 80, 81, 82, 83
Jurassic rocks 21

K

K/T boundary 13, 21, 23, 25
Kelleher Mesa 15
Kenton, Oklahoma 46
Ketchum, Thomas E. "Black Jack" 56, 73
Kiowa Mesa 15, 82
Kiowa National Grasslands 51, 72, 85

L

Lake Maloya 24, 25
Laramide orogeny 41, 66
Larga Mesa 4, 15, 60, 82, 83
Laughlin Peak 5, 6, 16, 28, 60, 77, 80, 82,
    83
Little Grande 76, 77

M

malpais 3, 8, 90
Malpais Mountain 28
Malpie Mountain 77
Manco Burro Pass 27
McJunkin, George 30, 31
McLaughlin Bridge 67
McNees Crossing 47, 50, 51
Meloche Mesa 24, 83, 84
Mesa de Maya 16, 27, 41, 77
Mesozoic Era 12
Mesozoic rocks 1, 12, 22, 85
Metcalf, Bill 36
Mills Canyon 85
Miocene Epoch 15
Morrison Formation 13, 15, 21, 33, 37, 38,
    39, 40, 41, 43, 44, 45, 47, 48, 53, 56,
    65, 66
Moses Church 51
Mount Marcy 62
Mt. Dora 4, 6, 9, 52, 67, 68, 70, 74, 75, 76
Mt. Taylor 4, 5, 9
Mud Hill 55, 59, 63
Mud Hill basalt 34

N

National Park Service 61, 93
Niobrara Formation 13, 14, 20, 32
North Canadian River 21, 47, 50, 51, 66, 67

O

Oak Canyon Mesa 4, 6, 15, 30, 32, 34, 35,
    55
Ogallala Formation 14, 15, 20, 21, 30, 32,
    35, 47, 48, 49, 51, 52, 67, 68, 70, 74,
    76, 77, 80, 81
oil and gas 12, 24, 47, 54, 93
Oklahoma panhandle 3, 27
Oligocene 15
ornithopod dinosaurs 11

P

Painted Desert 39
Palo Blanco Mountain 16, 28, 60, 77, 80, 82
Permian Basin 12, 54
Pierre Shale 13, 14, 20, 23, 25, 32, 71, 84, 86
Pope, Captain John 36
Precambrian rocks 3, 11
pressure ridges 3, 6, 8, 9, 62
Profazi Ranch 26
Purgatoire Formation 13, 21, 35, 36, 37, 38, 39, 47, 53, 56, 57, 66, 67
Purvine Hills 5, 6, 32, 34, 35, 36, 38, 54, 58
Purvine Hills Basalt 34, 35, 36, 55

R

Rabbit Ear Peak 5, 6, 7, 9, 17, 47, 49, 51, 52, 62, 66, 67, 68, 70, 74, 75, 76
Raton Basalt 16, 20, 22, 24, 25, 26, 27, 28, 29, 30, 32, 34, 35, 36, 37, 38, 41, 42, 54, 55, 56, 59, 60, 63, 71, 78, 80, 81, 82, 83, 84, 85, 86
Raton Basin 11, 24, 25, 27, 35, 79
Raton Creek 23
Raton Formation 7, 13, 23, 25
Raton Pass 1, 13, 21, 22, 51, 56, 86
Raton, city of 1, 11, 18, 19, 20, 21, 22, 86
Raton-age basalts 6, 15, 16, 49
Red Mountain 6, 28, 82
Red Mountain Dacite 7, 28, 82, 84, 85
Robinson Peak 9, 28, 30, 34, 54, 59, 60, 63
Rocky Mountains 1, 11, 30, 49, 84
Rooke, Sarah (Sally) 58
Round Mountain 67

S

San Andres Formation 12
sandstone dikes 42, 44
Sangre de Cristo Mountains 11, 12, 14, 15, 27, 48, 79, 83, 84

Santa Fe Group 15
Santa Fe Railroad 21
Santa Fe Trail 1, 20, 21, 22, 35, 36, 41, 47, 49, 50, 51, 52, 55, 67, 68, 72, 74, 75, 76, 81, 86, 87
Seven L Buttes 41
Sheep Mountain 28
Sheep Pen Sandstone 21, 43, 44, 45, 46
Shield volcanoes 3, 4, 5, 77
Sierra Clayton 5, 6, 9, 28, 76
Sierra Grande 4, 6, 7, 11, 14, 15, 17, 28, 30, 32, 34, 35, 49, 52, 58, 62, 66, 67, 71, 74, 76, 77, 78, 79, 80, 82
Sierra Grande arch 11, 14, 15, 35, 79, 80
slickensides 42
Sloan Canyon 44
Sloan Canyon Creek 44
Sloan Canyon Formation 21, 43, 44, 45, 46
squeeze-ups 59
St. John's Methodist Episcopal Church 28, 29
Steamboat Butte 41, 43
Stratovolcanoes 3, 4, 5
Sugarite Canyon State Park 13, 24, 25, 92

T

The Craters 5
theropod dinosaurs 69
Timber Buttes 28, 60, 82
Toll Gate Canyon 33, 36, 37
Towndrow Mountain 16, 27, 28
Travesser Canyon 41, 65
Travesser Creek 41, 66
Travesser Formation 21, 40, 41, 42, 43, 44, 65
Trinchera Creek 5, 17
Trinchera Pass 30, 79, 81
Trinidad Sandstone 20, 22, 24, 25, 26, 27, 71, 84, 85, 86
Twin Mountain 5, 6, 32, 33, 34, 35, 36, 53, 54, 55, 63
Twin Mountain Basalt 35, 36, 55, 58

U

Union County Court House 72

V

Valley post office 42
Valley School 46
Van Cleve Flow 77, 78

W

Wedding Cake Butte 20, 43, 44
Willow Springs 21, 86
Wooten Toll Road 22, 56
Wooten, "Uncle Dick" 1, 21
WPA 46, 73, 87

Y

Yankee Volcano 17, 25, 26

Z

Zion National Park 37, 48

PHOTOS & ILLUSTRATIONS

Unless otherwise noted, all illustrations were produced by the staff of the New Mexico Bureau of Geology and Mineral Resources.

Paul Bauer 75

Ron Blakey 12, 39, 48

Colorado Historical Society 79 (right)

Gina D'Ambrosio vii

Denver Museum of Natural History 31, 45 (painting by Jeff Wrona)

Folsom Museum 57, 58 (bottom)

William K. Hartmann 13

Adriel Heisey 2, 8, 15, 42, 44, 51 (top), 63 (right), 70, 74, 78, 84

George H.H. Huey cover, 39, 69 (top)

Virgil Lueth i, 7

Don MacCarter 62 (top)

William Muehlberger 5, 22, 23, 24 (top), 25, 26, 27, 28, 33 (top), 35 (top), 37, 38, 40, 43 (top), 45 (bottom), 47, 55, 56, 58 (right), 62 (bottom), 63 (left), 64, 69 (left), 73 (top), 80, 83

National Park Service 60

New Mexico Bureau of Geology and Mineral Resources photo archives 24 (bottom)

New York Public Library 50 (bottom), back cover

Laurence Parent iii, x, 4, 81

L. Greer Price 23 (bottom), 29, 30, 32 (right), 33 (bottom), 35 (bottom), 41, 43 (bottom), 51 (bottom), 59 (top), 65, 67, 77, 85

John Sibbick 69 (bottom)

William Stone 59 (bottom), 72

Union County Historical Society 73 (bottom)

University of Utah Press 10 (painting by Carel Brest van Kempen)

U.S. Geological Survey 6, 32 (left)

Melvin C. Warren 79 (painting)

LeRoy Wood, Driftwood Photography 46

ACKNOWLEDGMENTS

Our thanks to the museums in Raton, Clayton, and Folsom for helping us acquire valuable historic data to liven up this guide. Kay Thompson at the Folsom Museum and D. Ray Blakely at the Union County Historical Society were particularly gracious in helping us to acquire images as well. We gratefully acknowledge the help of the Denver Museum of Natural History in acquiring images that were both vital to the book and otherwise unobtainable. The staff of the parks and monuments in northeast New Mexico were also very helpful, in particular Jane Kwak at Capulin Volcano National Monument, who critiqued the earlier (1961) version of this guide; the staff of Sugarite Canyon State Park (the numerous pamphlets available at the park are a mine of pertinent information); and the staff at Clayton Lake State Park. Thanks also to the NPS staff at Harpers Ferry Center for their assistance in providing the park map for Capulin Volcano National Monument.

Many of the staff at the New Mexico Bureau of Geology and Mineral Resources were enormously helpful in gathering and developing materials for this volume, and in reviewing portions of the manuscript. These include Paul Bauer, Brian Brister, Ron Broadhead, Richard Chamberlin, Nelia Dunbar, Kathy Glesener, Steve Hook, Virgil Lueth, Bill McIntosh, and Peter Scholle. Many thanks to Gina d'Ambrosio for her diligent help in searching out photos and illustrations. We are grateful to those from outside the bureau who reviewed portions of the manuscript, including David T. Kirkpatrick at Human Systems Research, Inc., and both Adrian Hunt and Spencer Lucas at the New Mexico Museum of Natural History & Science.

A number of photographers submitted outstanding photos for this book, and these images have contributed enormously to the success of the book. Special thanks must go to Adriel Heisey, who provided his particular brand of expertise in the low-altitude aerial photos that are scattered throughout the book. We gratefully acknowledge his efforts on our behalf, which went above and beyond any reasonable expectations.

ABOUT THE AUTHORS

William R. Muehlberger, faculty member for 38 years with the Department of Geological Sciences at the University of Texas at Austin, is the Peter T. Flawn Chair in Geology Emeritus. He and his students have mapped large areas of northern New Mexico from the eastern San Juan Basin (Chama Basin) eastward over the Tusas Mountains to Ojo Caliente, the Taos Plateau, and across northeastern New Mexico. He uses this region to teach the new classes of astronauts about geologic processes. NASA has awarded him the Exceptional Scientific Achievement Medal for his Apollo work and the Distinguished Service Medal for his Space Shuttle crew lectures and field trips. He has received the Best Paper Award from both the Geological Society of America and the American Association of Petroleum Geologists, as well as several teaching awards.

Sally J. Muehlberger, who has a bachelors degree in English literature from Scripps College, Claremont, California and a masters in Library Science from the University of Texas at Austin, researched the Indian, Spanish, and American histories of the region to provide information on the colorful heritage of northeastern New Mexico.

L. Greer Price is currently senior geologist and chief editor at the New Mexico Bureau of Geology and Mineral Resources, where he manages the publishing program. Prior to coming to the bureau, Greer spent four years as managing editor at Grand Canyon Association, ten years with the National Park Service, and eight years as a geologist in the oil patch. His varied career has involved teaching, writing, and field work throughout North America. He is the author of *An Introduction to Grand Canyon Geology.*

GEOLOGIC TIME			GEOLOGIC RECORD		ROCK TYPE	EVENTS
		Quaternary	Alluvium	Raton-Clayton volcanics	basalt, andesite, and dacite	Eruption of Raton/Clayton volcanic field
	CENOZOIC	Tertiary	Ogallala Fm.		sand and gravel with some silt and clay	High Plains Aquifer
			Poison Canyon		sandstone and conglomerate	AGE OF MAMMALS
		Cretaceous	Raton Formation		sandstone, siltstone, mudstone, and shale	K/T Boundary, Cretaceous extinctions
			Vermejo Formation		sandstone, shale, and coal	Laramide Orogeny
			Trinidad Sandstone		sandstone	
			Pierre Shale		shale	
	MESOZOIC		Niobrara Formation (incl. Ft. Hays Limestone)		limestone and shale	
		Jurassic	Carlisle Shale		shale	
			Greenhorn Formation		limestone	Western Interior Seaway
			Graneros Shale		shale	
		Triassic	DAKOTA GROUP	Romeroville Sandstone	sandstone	Dinosaur trackways at Clayton Lake
				Pajarito Formation	sandstone	
				Mesa Rica Sandstone	sandstone	
		Permian	Purgatoire Formation		sandstone, shale, and coal	
			Morrison Formation		sandstone, siltstone, and shale	The most important uranium deposits in New Mexico occur in Morrison Formation sandstones in the vicinity of Grants
		Pennsylvanian	Entrada Sandstone		sandstone	
		Mississippian	CHINLE GROUP	Sheep Pen Sandstone	sandstone	
	PALEOZOIC	Devonian		Sloan Canyon Fm.	sandstone	Phytosaur remains
				Travesser Formation	sandstone	Rocks of the Painted Desert in NE Arizona are of this age
		Silurian		Baldy Hill Formation		Permian extinctions
		Ordovician	Sangre de Cristo Formation (Pennsylvanian – Permian)		sandstone, shale, and limestone	Ancestral rocks of Paleozoic age underlie the entire field trip area but are not exposed.
		Cambrian				Rocks of Paleozoic age are well exposed in SE New Mexico and West Texas
		Precambrian	Exposed in the Sangre de Cristo Mountains to the west		Granites, metasediments, and metavolcanics	

Geologic time scale (Millions of years):
Present, 66, 145, 210, 245, 286, 325, 360, 410, 440, 505, 544, 4600

(Not to scale)